Rudolf Steiner
Scientist of the Invisible

A P Shepherd

Rudolf Steiner

Scientist of the Invisible

Floris Classics

First published as *A Scientist of the Invisible*
in 1954 by Hodder & Stoughton Ltd, London
Reprinted with an introduction by Owen Barfield
in 1983 and 1991 by Floris Books, Edinburgh

British Library CIP Data available

ISBN 0-86315-518-9

Printed in Great Britain
by Billing & Sons Ltd, Worcester

CONTENTS

ACKNOWLEDGMENTS

For permission to use extracts contained in this book, the author and publishers are indebted to:

Anthroposophical Press, New York, publishers of *Reincarnation as a Phenomenon of Metamorphosis*, by Dr. G. Wachsmuth.

Cambridge University Press, publishers of *Physics and Philosophy* by Sir James Jeans.

Faber and Faber Limited, publishers of *Liturgy and Society* by A. G. Hebert.

Geoffrey Bles Limited, publishers of *Dream and Reality* by Nicolas Berdyaev.

John Murray Limited, publishers of *Belief in Christ*, by Charles Gore.

Macmillan & Company Limited, publishers of *The River Line* by Charles Morgan and *Collected Poems* by A. E., for which we should like to thank also Mr. Diarmuid Russell.

Rudolf Steiner—Nachlassverwaltung, the Literary Executors of Rudolf Steiner, for permission to quote from two of his books: *The Mission of Folk Souls* and *Atlantis and Lemuria*.

Rudolf Steiner Publishing Company, publishers of *An Outline of Occult Science* by Rudolf Steiner.

Vincent Stuart Limited, publishers of *Living Time* by Maurice Nicoll.

FOREWORD

MORE than a quarter of a century has elapsed since the first publication of this book, whose one aim (as the author observes in his Preface) was "to break down the barrier of ignorance and indifference" that conceals from the majority of English people the teaching of Rudolf Steiner.

Since that date certain changes have occurred in the situation it was designed to meet. On the one hand the general confidence in a positivist or reductionist view of reality has eroded a little further; on the other the barrier of ignorance and indifference is a little less compacted than it was. But in both cases it is only a little; much too little to make *A Scientist of the Invisible* a less important book than it was at the time of its first appearance, though enough to justify expectation of its reaching a wider public than the first edition could hope to achieve.

When I began lecturing in American universities in 1964, I used to encounter educated men who had never even heard the name of Rudolf Steiner. Then years later this no longer happened. Such books as Theodore Roszak's *Where the Wasteland Ends,* Fritjof Capra's *The Tao of Physics,* Morris Berman's *The Re-enchantment of the World,* Trevor Levere's *Poetry Realized in Nature,* to name only a few I happen to have read in the last ten years, are perhaps only straws in the wind, but the wind of change is real enough to have lifted them. The truth is that many more minds are opening to the realization that an altogether new way of thinking is desperately needed. Unfortunately not many of them are untrammelled enough to realize also that a new way of thinking is likely to reveal a new and unfamiliar world. They overlook the simple, if annoying, fact that, if its consequences were *not* unfamiliar and therefore, at first encounter, shocking, it would not *be* a new way of thinking — only the old one in a grand new dress. It is this inability, or refusal, to control impatience long enough to let in study and reflection that appears to be responsible for the blindness of the western world to what concerns it so nearly.

Most people who are at all well acquainted with Steiner's writings, and known to be so, have experienced more than once what it is to be asked "Where shall I begin?" by someone in whom the indifference has begun to weaken while the ignorance is still total. Many of them will have had like me a helpless feeling about replying because of the enormous variety and scope of those writings and reported lecture-cycles, not to speak of the ever increasing volume of anthroposophical literature being produced by his followers. There may perhaps be some special interest or knowledge in the enquirer which makes it appropriate to refer him to a particular book or lecture-cycle by Steiner himself. If so, all the better. Where there is not, it may well be wiser for him to read in the first place something *about* the Austrian seer and philosopher, what he set out to do, what he did, and the consequences that have begun to flow from it.

For such a purpose it is difficult to imagine a better book than this one. It is so unassuming, so thorough for all its brevity, so *workmanlike.* There is moreover in the manner of presentation that extra tinge of authority, based on ingrained conviction, which can colour, without their willing it, the utterance of those who have found in spiritual science some truth they had discovered for themselves before they encountered it. It reads smoothly and consecutively enough, but it must have been a formidable task to combine in some two hundred pages a not inadequate account of, first, the method of spiritual science — or, to give it its other name, Anthroposophy — and the substance of its findings at the date of Steiner's death; secondly, its application in numerous practical activities; and thirdly, the life and character of the man Rudolf Steiner. It is a task in which I feel Canon Shepherd succeeded.

Anyone reading the Contents page will notice that I have changed the order in which these three separate but allied subjects are dealt with. I am now going to go further and suggest to any reader coming quite fresh to it all, that he adopts yet a third order in his perusal. After the first two chapters I would recommend him to go on to chapters XVI and XVII (the application), to continue with chapters IX to XV (or, if he has little interest in the churches,

IX to XIV), and to conclude with III to VIII on Steiner himself and the Anthroposophical Society. I hope it is a sensible suggestion. I do not think the fate of the book depends on its being adopted, but it might hasten its impact.

And that, I believe, is something that is badly needed. As the result of a good many years of increasing, though still painfully inadequate penetration into the vastness and depth of Steiner's legacy and of anxious reflection on it, I have become convinced of this: that the future of civilisation depends, more than anything else, on its willingness or unwillingness to make of that legacy the kind of use which its nature demands — a use different in mode but not less abiding than the use that was made by an earlier age of the legacies of Pythagoras and Aristotle. I can only hope therefore that this book, by achieving a deservedly wide circulation, will help to shame the impatience and compel the study and reflection.

Owen Barfield

South Darenth, Kent
November 1982

PREFACE

My first contact with Rudolf Steiner and his teaching was casual. I do not think it was accidental. A book which I had written on the problem of Time had just been published (1941) and I was discussing its content with a group of men. In the course of the discussion one of them said, "Your idea, that the whole of our earthly life is recovered after death as a unity and as an actual experience, is the same as Rudolf Steiner's." "Who," I asked, "is Rudolf Steiner?" It was not long before I found out and began to study his teaching, and was amazed to discover that what I had presented as a hypothesis, arising out of the study of a problem, was known to him in direct spirit-perception and carried to far higher levels of understanding than mere hypothesis could ever attain. The link made me a convinced student of Anthroposophy. I could not understand, however, how with a University education and a fairly wide range of reading, I had never heard of this remarkable man nor his work.

Some two years later, I was discussing my book with the late Archbishop William Temple, who had been kind enough to write a foreword to it. I spoke of its confirmation in the teaching of Steiner. He was exceedingly interested and said to me, "You know, I have often been told that I ought to read Steiner. I must really begin." A year later I met him again and he said, "I am really going to start on Steiner." Shortly afterwards came the tragedy of his sudden death.

My perplexity was increased. Here was a man, one of the ablest, most broad-minded and most widely-learned men of his day, with a knowledge of German, who had only casually heard of Rudolf Steiner, and knew nothing about his teaching. So it was everywhere. Except for the few who were students of Anthroposophy, I found that practically no educated man of my acquaintance knew anything about Steiner, while the one or two criticisms I read of him were based on a single reading of one of his books, which had been interpreted without any real understanding of its background.

I felt that there was a barrier of mind, especially among English people. The accepted scientific materialism of our day, coupled with the factual realism of the English temperament, constituted a barrier to any consideration of Steiner and his work. He was labelled a "crank" and dismissed from their minds. Yet I was more and more convinced that what Steiner had taught was vital to the needs of mankind today. I determined to attempt to write an introduction to Steiner and his work that would break through this barrier of indifference, and provide, for the ordinary man, a background against which his writings could be studied. In this I was encouraged by the publishers of my own book.

The task proved much greater than I had anticipated. A mere journalistic presentation of the man and his work might create some interest, but it would not be sufficient to overcome suspicion and to persuade the reader to pursue further his own study of the subject. For that there must, in the first place, be sufficient biographical information for the reader to perceive how Steiner's knowledge of the spiritual had developed out of his own consciousness. There must also be a sufficiently detailed and frank exposition of the main substance of his teaching, considered in relation to modern scientific and logical thinking.

This meant a much more serious and prolonged undertaking, only made possible by the boundless patience of my publishers. Now that it is complete, I am aware of its many deficiencies, which will be even more apparent to those who have been students of Anthroposophy far longer than I.

I should like to express my thanks to those who have read through the MS. and have made invaluable suggestions: Mildred Kirkcaldy, Dorothy Osmond, Owen Barfield, Thomas Lawson and George Adams. Their help has much improved the book, but I alone am responsible for its remaining mistakes and omissions. Such are inevitable in any attempt to write an introduction to so vast and deep a subject. My one aim has been to break down the barrier of ignorance and indifference, that conceals from the majority of English people the teaching of this profound and scientifically-minded seer and thinker. If I have, to any degree, succeeded in doing this, my purpose will be accomplished.

Worcester. February, 1954.

CHAPTER I

HUMANITY BEWILDERED

FOR the last thirty years thoughtful men have prophesied an impending crisis in the life of Humanity. As would be expected, a great number have written from the point of view of religion, for, in view of the growing disregard of the ordinary man for religion and for the ideal and other-worldly standards of Christianity, the religious prophet must inevitably see in the present situation calamity and judgment.

But warnings have been uttered by other voices. In 1935 a remarkable book, *Man the Unknown*, was written by an American scientist, Alexis Carrel. This book ran into many editions and was translated into many languages. It was a brilliant survey (chiefly illustrated from the U.S.A.) of the civilisation which has been produced by scientific discoveries and conclusions and by modern education. It painted a gloomy picture of a degenerating humanity, and pointed out that humanity, like the human body, did not react inevitably against degenerative influences. It declared that "Science has created a world to which man does not belong", and called upon scientists to widen the range of their studies, to reconsider their facts and re-think their conclusions, before this human degeneracy got out of control.

A more recent challenge and warning was given in the book, *The Yogi and the Commissar*, by Arthur Koestler, in which the author paints the bewilderment of humanity, between the rival claims of a return to Eastern other-worldly mysticism, or an advance to a ruthlessly-planned society, evolved out of the logic of Western scientific materialism.

Since the last war there has been a general flutter in the scientific dovecots. The terrible reality of the atomic bomb and the still greater possibilities of atomic power, known only to themselves, alarmed the scientists into uttering a warning to mankind and proclaiming the need of a world-wide control of man's new powers. But the violence of nations and the rumble of war still persist, and the scientist has been largely silenced by the need, or even the compulsion, of serving his country under the enforced secrecy of preparation for the next war.

Meanwhile what about the ordinary man? It is the tragedy of the ordinary man that he never listens to the warnings of the prophets until the doom is upon him, and then he is too terrified to listen and too stupefied to understand—and in any case it is too late! Today he needs no prophet to convince him that he is face to face with world-catastrophe and disaster. Having barely survived a second world war, he is even more bewildered to find that, after nine years of peace, the situation remains alarming and dangerous. Much of the civilisation of Europe lies in ruin, across which the two colossi of the East and the West growl at one another, filling the air with threats and suspicions. It seems to the ordinary man that he will have to seek refuge with one or the other, but he hesitates. One embodies the secret police, the concentration camps, and the ruthless regimentation of the individual, which he hoped the war had overcome; the other, for all its political liberty and material prosperity, looks to many too like the last citadel of pre-war capitalism. On all sides social, national, and racial hatreds and suspicions are boiling over and the economic world-situation seems quite insoluble. For himself, as an individual, there seems no security or hope or even concern.

But the bewilderment of the human outlook today goes deeper than the tragedy of the immediate situation. It is a bewilderment which that tragedy only accentuates, and which peace and prosperity can only dangerously conceal. It arises from the fact that man today has no background of thought in regard to his origin or destiny, against which he can assess the present situation. He can only see it as an immediate menace to his very existence, by forces which he can neither understand nor resist. Western man today has no philosophy of life that can sustain or encourage him.

As a result of modern education and the popularisation of science, mankind as a whole has accepted the scientific point of view, which explains man in terms of the physical world in which he lives, and of his own physical being. For most people of average education their scientific outlook is that of science forty years ago. For them, the earth is seen as situated in a vast physical universe, entirely determined by unchanging Natural Law, and most of it having no relation to, or concern with, this small planet in one of its many solar systems. Yet the life of this small planet itself is represented in terms of millions of years, stretching into past and future, in which the existence of humanity has appeared at a comparatively recent date in its history, and long before the end of that history will have ceased to exist. Man had his origin in material evolution, and will come to an end in it as a mere chapter of its history.

But this chapter, the life story of Mankind, itself runs into millennia, in which civilisation after civilisation have succeeded one another, without any ordered sequence or significance that the scientist or the historian can discover, and without any indication of what the future may hold. Meanwhile the life of each individual is only some seventy years —and today probably less than that—and that short span is the individual's sole share in, and concern with, the life of Mankind and the evolution of the Earth. What importance can be placed upon himself in such an endless chain of material existence? What reasonable claim can he have to be taken seriously?

There are two factors in Man which contend against this pessimistic outlook, but today, for the most part, they fight a losing battle. The first factor is man's instinct for life, love, happiness, and, in most men, for goodness. Especially in youth, these instincts are very strong and persistent, but in many today the years of disillusionment and disappointment have either overwhelmed them, or are driving men to seek for their realisation in one or other of the violent ideologies, which have been the immediate cause of the world disaster. If, on the other hand, men turn to their reason for a justification of these instincts, science tells them that their instincts are an illusion, merely the result of wishful thinking.

The second factor in human life which denies pessimism is religion. Unfortunately, in the eyes of Western humanity, religion was discredited in the prosperous, easy days of scientific self-satisfaction, as unscientific in its assumptions and methods, and as no longer necessary or even useful. This attitude to religion has abated in many scientific quarters, but the popular assumptions remain.

Even for many who are regularly attached to religious bodies, religion has become a matter of feeling, sustained by belief, while their thinking is absorbed by scientific concepts and external activities. There is within them a hopeless dualism of thinking and feeling. Moreover, religion seems to them to deal with a future, non-earthly existence, and to have little to say about the real significance and possibilities of the earthly material life, in which even the religious man is immersed for almost the whole of his time. Religion has, for the most part, accepted the conclusions of Science about man's physical evolution, adding to them its own faith in a future spirit-life, which will provide—for the religious man—a better destiny. But to the majority of those unattached to it, religion seems to be unrelated to the stress and strain, the immediate interests, the tremendous prizes, the continual risks, which the material, scientifically-controlled life involves. Moreover, owing to this dualism of feeling and thinking, the ethical standards of humanity have become confused, and thereby the influence of religion has been still further reduced.

For the uneducated masses of humanity, the situation is somewhat different. For them the physical life is always completely absorbing—and usually exhausting—and religion seems to them to be—like art and music—an "extra", for those who happen to like it and to have time for it. Meanwhile the masses have been the most helpless victims of the present world disaster, and today they stand bewildered and alarmed, and ready to panic into any plausible policy of violence.

Alexis Carrel was right. "Science has made for Man a world to which he does not belong." Man cannot see in the world any place or meaning for himself, commensurate with his own instincts for life and happiness, his own highest ideals, or the importance which religion attributes to him.

Not a few remedies are offered for this world dilemma, but most of them are merely a reiteration of the idealistic creeds which the last thirty years seem to have overwhelmed —humanism, democracy, universal education, social planning. Religion reasserts its own traditional position, sometimes with a stiffening attitude towards its dogmas and discipline, sometimes with a rather pathetic optimism about the spiritual efficacy of more up-to-date, scientific methods of evangelism and organisation. But all these remedies still accept the scientific explanation of the physical origin of man and the world, and leave the dualism of feeling and thinking in regard to religion and science still unsolved. One remedy solves this dualism,—by denying the reality of half of it. That remedy is Communism, the logical political and social expression of scientific materialism.

As we have already indicated, scientific thought itself has passed through many revolutions since the beginning of this century, and most of our foremost scientists no longer hold the materialistic and determinist philosophy of nineteenth-century science, which still colours popular secular thought. While, however, the modern scientist himself is far less certain of his ground, many people who are aware of the latest scientific developments, assume that they possess a certainty of explanation which they do not claim. A book, entitled *Physics and Philosophy*, by Sir James Jeans, published in 1942, surveys the growth and development of the latest scientific thought, and in particular explains the revolutionary conclusions of the New Physics of this century. The author, however, is at pains to make it clear that the latest theories of physics do not give any picture or explanation of *reality*, but are simply mathematical explanations of the pattern of events, that is, of the way in which reality manifests itself to our senses. "Our studies can never put us into contact with reality," he declared, "we can never understand what events are, *until man becomes endowed with more senses than he at present possesses.*"

But this more modest and guarded outlook of science leaves man even more bewildered and with even less philosophy of life, as he faces the world today. We cannot do better than quote from the conclusion to the book.

> The plain fact is that there are no conclusions. If we must state a conclusion, it would be that many of the former conclusions of nineteenth-century science on philosophical questions are once again in the melting-pot. . . . We can hardly say that the new physics justifies any new conclusions on determinism, causality or free-will, but we can say that the argument for determinism is in some respects less compelling than it seemed to be fifty years ago. There appears to be a case for reopening the whole question as soon as anyone can discover how to do so.
>
> This may seem a disappointing harvest to have garnered from so extensive a field of new scientific activity, and from one, moreover, which comes so close to the territory of philosophy. Yet we may reflect that physics and philosophy are at most a few thousand years old, but probably have lives of thousands of millions of years stretching away in front of them. They are only just beginning to get under way, and we are still, in Newton's words, like little children playing with pebbles on the sea-shore, while the great ocean of truth rôlls, unexplored, beyond our reach. It can hardly be a matter of surprise that our race has not succeeded in solving any large part of its most difficult problems in the first millionth part of its existence. Perhaps life would be a duller affair if it had, for to many it is not knowledge, but the quest for knowledge, that gives the greater interest to thought. To travel hopefully is better than to arrive.

This complacent scientific agnosticism can give no satisfying answer to the present human bewilderment. It still identifies the evolution of man with the physical evolution of the earth, though it thrusts back the origin of that evolution into an even deeper uncertainty. Its contented contemplation of the uncertainties of humanity's millennial future offers no consolation or guidance in regard to the menace of the present situation to the individual's short span of life, and no justification to his instinctive moral and spiritual beliefs. Finally, the gulf is even wider between the physicist's absorption in constructing a mathematical logical picture of the pattern of events, and the Christian gospel, with its ethics and otherworldly certainties, based on revelation and faith.

The only answer that could meet the present bewilderment of humanity would be a scientific explanation of the Universe and of Man which would justify Man's instinctive faith in the absolute worth of individual personality; and an integration of religion into that viewpoint, not by denying the supernatural beliefs and claims of religion, but by finding them justified in the scientific world-concept. That such an answer could be found, most scientists would regard as an impossible, and many religious thinkers as a presumptuous, expectation.

As a matter of fact, such an answer has been given—by a man with the widest scientific knowledge and the most thorough training in scientific thinking, who thought, spoke, and wrote as a scientist. That man was Rudolf Steiner, and the purpose of this book is to consider his answer.

CHAPTER II

A MAN WITH AN ANSWER

IF any answer to the problem of Man and the Universe can be found which will solve the bewilderment of humanity and remove the dualism between Religion and Science, we cannot but expect its conclusions to be startling and original. Such the conclusions of Rudolf Steiner certainly are, but it must be remembered all through, that in all his teaching it is to the test of clear and unprejudiced thinking that Steiner appeals.

Steiner thought, spoke, and wrote as a scientist. Though he challenged many of the conclusions of science, he did so as one who knew at first-hand the whole trend of scientific thought. Born only a few years after the publication of Darwin's *Origin of Species*, educated in science at an Austrian Secondary School and at the Technical University at Vienna, the early years of his original thinking were the years when German thought was absorbing and developing Darwinian ideas, under the leadership of Haeckel, with whom Steiner was well acquainted. He lived through the subsequent years of Einstein's discovery of Relativity and of the first emergence of the New Physics, and long enough to see the confusion which the New Physics wrought in the once confidently accepted belief in materialistic determinism. He had a life-long admiration for the patience, honesty, and thoroughness of scientific investigation, and, in regard to Haeckel he expressed this admiration so definitely, that in later years he was accused—quite falsely—of having been himself at that time a disciple of materialistic determinism. Although his own investigations carried him into fields far beyond the range of physical science, he always carried into these investigations, and into the application of them to physical phenomena, the concepts and methods of scientific thought.

In later chapters of this book the various aspects of Steiner's thought and teaching will be considered at greater length. Meanwhile it will be helpful to set out quite shortly the full range of the answer which he gives to the problem which confronts us.

In the first place he widens the frontiers of knowledge. He declares that the phenomena, perceivable by us through our physical senses and deducible by thought from those perceptions, do not constitute the whole range of the actual realities of our universe. Behind the physical realities which we perceive—yet integrally related to them and as objectively real—there are supersensible realities. They too are directly perceptible, but only by senses other than the physical. This assertion Steiner makes, not as a hypothesis, but as a result of direct personal perception of these supersensible realities. This supersensory perception which he possessed can, he maintains, be acquired by others by the method of conscious, concentrated thinking along certain lines. At a future stage of human evolution it will be a universal faculty of mankind.

These new horizons reveal new knowledge about ourselves and the world in which we live. Perhaps the most challenging item of this new knowledge is the definite assertion that man —and the physical world—had a spiritual, and not a material, origin, and that both have a spiritual destiny. It may appear a presumption to challenge a scientific theory so well-established as that of evolution, viz. that higher forms of life and consciousness have evolved out of the lower forms of material substance, whether directly or by the "leaps" of emergent evolution. Nevertheless, Steiner, while accepting all the facts that science has discovered, does challenge the conclusions drawn from them, and his point of view involves a complete re-thinking, not only of the origin of physical and mental phenomena, but of many apparently established conclusions based upon the accepted theory of evolution. He sets out his own point of view with a wealth of description and fact. Some of it is derived from supersensible perception, and as such cannot be directly tested, but all of it is related to observable phenomena, in such a way that it is capable of just as sound confirmation from these phenomena, as that which Science can produce in favour of the generally accepted theory of evolution.

From such a radical divergence from accepted opinion one would expect startling conclusions to follow. The first of these is in regard to man's own being and nature. Having given man a spirit-origin[1] and an age-long evolution from a purely supersensible environment to his present material existence in the physical world, Steiner is able to see and to reveal to us the nature of Man's present being, as compact of both the spiritual and the material, the elements working into each other in a visible unity, varying in their function and in their ultimate destiny, but all of them alike, objectively real and perceivable.

Moreover he shows that man shares these elements in varying degrees with the physical world and the life manifested in it, and is in that way far more intimately related to his environment than the materialistic outlook of our day imagines. Forces stream into his being, not only from the animal and vegetable world and from the earth itself, but from the surrounding atmosphere and from the great cosmos of sun and stars, which man today has come to regard as "meaningless masses" whose irrelevant hugeness denies him importance.

The essence of man's earthly evolution Steiner shows to have been the evolution of human consciousness, the life of the human soul. He traces this as a descent from a supersensible awareness of the beings and activities of his spirit-environment and a relatively dim apprehension of the physical world—into an increasingly conscious perception and understanding of his material environment, and a consequent dimming of his supersensible perception. Before him now lies the possibility of a re-ascent, in his achieved self-awareness, to a higher level of consciousness and existence, in which he will have spiritualised the various elements of his being—

[1] The word "spirit"—alone or compounded with other words—almost always signifies in this book the "supersensible", an existent reality, whether expressed in sense-phenomena or existing apart from them, which cannot be perceived by the physical senses.

including his physical body—into a perfection of free and fully-conscious spirit-being. With such a concept of spirit-origin and exalted spirit-destiny, man is delivered from the self-contempt and self-pity to which materialistic concepts have brought him. Moreover he is seen to hold in himself the clue to the understanding of the mysteries of cosmic life. Let man but truly know and understand himself and the nature of his being, declared Steiner, and he will find that he holds within himself the clue to the secrets of the universe—he is the microcosm within the macrocosm.

As a result of this new understanding of man, Steiner throws an entirely new light upon history. It is no longer primarily the story of man's increasing knowledge of and mastery over his material environment—although that remains a dominant fact of history. History is primarily the story of the evolution of the consciousness of Humanity towards self-conscious freedom of being, the attainment of which by man is the whole purpose of the existence of the material world. With such a clue to the understanding of history, the sequence of civilisations, the diversity of races, the emergence and variety of nationalities, and our present international problems and difficulties fall into a unity of spiritual evolution. Moreover history becomes not only an interpretation of the past, but, what it never yet has been, a clear pointer for the future.

In this new view of human history and of the origin of man and the universe, the dualism of religion and science, of secular and sacred, disappears. The whole world perceptible to the physical senses is seen to be in constant and immediate relation to the spirit world. Religion is the expression of the relation between the spirit-world and man, which was at first directly perceived by him, but later was conveyed by revelation and mystic experience through spiritual leaders, and expressed in the great world-religions. Even though no longer perceived or directly experienced by man, this spiritual relationship has always remained as an actual activity in, and concern with, the life of mankind on the part of the spirit world. The coming of Christ into human history is seen as the focal point of this relationship, the consummation of the divine approach to man of which the greatest spiritual leaders of humanity had continuously been aware. To Rudolf Steiner's spirit-perception the life and death and resurrection of Jesus Christ are seen to be the central happenings of all history, cosmic as well as earthly. On the spirit power released by that event the pattern and subsequent history of the earth and of the destiny of man depend. The earlier world-religions are seen, not as false or opposed to Christianity, nor as an equally eligible alternative, but as arising naturally out of the level of human consciousness in which they had their birth. In Christianity they are not denied, but fulfilled.

In this objective revelation of the supersensible realities working in and through human history, the individual human being holds a position of dignity and importance. His direct concern with the whole spiritual evolution of humanity is not limited to the few years of one earthly life. The individual is the warp, as his social life is the woof, of the web of human history. Rudolf Steiner sees the deed of Christ, as that which objectively delivers humanity and the earth-evolution from the inevitability of moral disintegration, and which alone offers to the individual deliverance from his past, and the possibility of final spiritual attainment.

Moreover, Steiner reveals an extension of the sphere of morality, which was not unknown to the ancient world, but which to modern ways of thinking would appear almost inconceivable, viz. the essential relation between morality and higher knowledge. The organs of supersensible perception are organs, not of the body, but of the soul. The structure of the soul is moral, and the possibility of true and conscious supersensible knowledge is conditioned by the attainment of the right moral qualities.

The application of these far-reaching discoveries in regard to the nature of man and the universe, to the practical activities of human life, has had far-reaching results. In education, in agriculture, in medicine, in the treatment of the mentally abnormal, in art, and in the solution of social problems, new principles and methods have been propounded and are being widely and successfully practised. We hope to deal with these in more detail in later chapters.

To his revelation of the objective reality of the supersensible world and of its relation to sense-perceived phenomena, and his explanation of the origin and destiny of man and all that flows from it, Steiner gave the name "Anthroposophy".[1] The significance of this name is that the secret of the universe is expressed in and discoverable by an understanding of the real nature of man. If Anthroposophy is true it supplies the answer to the present human dilemma. It extends the horizons of knowledge, it integrates the material with the spiritual, it resolves the dualism of science and religion, it restores dignity and significance to human life, it justifies the assumption of human instinct and of religion as to the eternal importance of the individual, and it disproves any political or social system that is based upon a materialistic conception of life or of history. Nothing could be more important than that mankind, and especially the leaders of human thought, should study and examine it.

It must be admitted, however, that there are considerable difficulties in the way of such study. The first difficulty is Steiner's statement that his teaching is based upon his immediate and direct perception of supersensible realities, that are not perceptible to the ordinary man. *Ipso facto*, the truth of this claim cannot be scientifically proved or disproved at the level of physical consciousness. There are other considerations, however, to be borne in mind. In the first place, if it is true, as Sir James Jeans says, that any real extension of knowledge waits upon the evolution or development of further senses of perception, we must not be surprised that, if anyone speaks out of the possession of such senses, we are not able directly to test the experience which he relates. Moreover, Steiner declares that the organs of supersensible perception, which in him, as in some other men and women, were already highly developed, are organs which in all of us await development,

[1] The expressions "Anthroposophy" and "Spiritual Science" were used interchangeably by Rudolf Steiner as descriptions of his teaching. They are so used all through this book.

and he gives detailed instructions as to how this may in full consciousness be taken in hand. Furthermore, in considering his teaching he especially warns his readers against credulous acceptance of what he reveals by supersensible perception. He urges them rather to consider with clear logical judgment the explanations and conclusions which the application of these supersensible revelations to material facts and phenomena produces, and to make these a test of the reliability of the supersensible revelations. Further, he declares that if these supersensible facts themselves be allowed to live in our minds—as, at least, experimental hypotheses, without either immediate acceptance or rejection—they will, of themselves and by the light they throw on other perceptible phenomena, bear witness to their own truth. At the lowest level they can be accepted as hypotheses in the normal method of science, and proved or rejected by their consequences and application.

Nevertheless, the fact, that at the outset we are confronted by a claim to direct perception of realities beyond sense-perception, does demand honest and critical examination. Such a claim must naturally be weighed, in the first place, by the character and personality of the man making it. Our first task, therefore, will be to give some account of the life and personality of Rudolf Steiner and of the evolution of his consciousness. Indeed such a biographical study is an almost essential introduction to his teaching, for it will simplify for the reader the comprehension of much in it that, taken by itself, must at first appear unfamiliar and even startling.

CHAPTER III

CHILDHOOD AND SCHOOLDAYS

THE main source of our knowledge of Rudolf Steiner's life is his own autobiography, which he wrote when he was about sixty years old. He explains in the opening sentences of the book that he had written it against his own personal inclinations, in order to give an authoritative answer to a number of criticisms of the cause to which he had devoted his life, criticisms which had been made on the ground of an alleged inconsistency between some of his earlier deeds and writings and his later teaching.

It is not difficult to see how these mistaken criticisms arose, and even in his own autobiography it is necessary to enter deeply into the process of his mental and spiritual evolution, in order to realise the fundamental consistency of his life. But we may be thankful for the occasion which compelled Rudolf Steiner to set out, without sentimentality or appraisement, this direct account of his spiritual pilgrimage. It is in itself an indispensable key and commentary to the sequence and substance of his writing and teaching. It is also a picture of the initiation of an exceptionally gifted human spirit into the deepest mysteries of man and the universe. It will not suffice to give an account of the external events of Steiner's life or of the impression he made upon his fellows. His real story is the story of his own inner life as he gives it to us, and to present this adequately will require detailed treatment, especially of the earlier part of his life.

Rudolf Steiner was the eldest of the three children of a village station-master in Austria, in the country south of Vienna. His earliest recollection was of the village of Pottschach, at the foot of the Styrian Alps, where he lived from his second to his eighth year. From his earliest years he lived a rather lonely existence, for the station-master's liability to be moved made him and his family strangers to the intimacies of those, who had spent all their life in one small community. But his life was in no way unhappy. The beauty of his surroundings appealed to him and, at the same time, the eager inquisitiveness of his mind found ample scope in the activity which surrounded the village station. The arrival or departure of a train was an event which attracted even the village notables, the priest, the schoolmaster, and the burgomaster, and then there was all the wonder and imagination which attached itself to those who came from and departed into the mysterious world into which the ribbon of the railway line disappeared. His childish mind was deeply interested in the inexplicable things which occupied grown-up people, the intricacies of the station office and—in the village itself—the friendly mill into which he was always welcome, and the yarn factory, which because he could never enter it, filled his mind with endless unanswered perplexities. "But," he writes, "I never asked questions about it. For it was my childish conviction that it does no good to ask questions about something which you cannot look at." Already there was the germ of that attitude of scientific realism that governed his whole life.

At the age of eight his father was moved to the station of Neudörfl, nearer to Vienna, but just over the Hungarian border. There the increasing national consciousness of the Hungarians made the Austrian station-master's son still more of an outsider to the village children than he had been in Pottshach. The result was that the little boy used to ramble alone through the woods, where he made friends with the wood-gatherers from the village and the servants from the castle. From them he learnt all the village gossip, which added considerably to the problems that puzzled his understanding.

There was something more, however, something much deeper, unknown and unsuspected by others, that lay behind the loneliness of Rudolf Steiner's childhood. It stamped the mark of that loneliness on his whole life. Rudolf Steiner is not the only person who could remember that in his earliest years he had had experiences and impressions of a reality other than that of the material world. Both Thomas Traherne and William Wordsworth wrote of such experiences.

> There was a time when meadow, grove and stream,
> The earth and every common sight
> To me did seem
> Apparelled in celestial light,
> The glory and the freshness of a dream.[1]

But even to these rare spirits, what they wrote about was only the memory of an experience which in later years had faded out. For most men and women there is no such memory and to our ordinary consciousness it all seems so unreal, that we are inclined to put down Wordsworth's words to poetic imagination. But in the case of Rudolf Steiner that experience was never blotted out; in fact, it was a continuously developing experience all through his life, the most real experience that he had, and it was to explain the course of its development that he wrote his autobiography.

As we have already seen, from his earliest years he was perplexed by the endless questions which occur to thoughtful children, the why and wherefore of the strange world in which they find themselves. In the case of most children these questions are soon overlaid by their interest in companionship with other children and by the absorption of their senses in their immediate material surroundings. But it was not so with Rudolf Steiner. Already at the age of eight, so he himself tells us, he was conscious of realities that differed from those of the material world, inasmuch as they were not available to touch or physical contact, but which were clear to his vision in a constant and consistently objective way, that left no doubt in him that they were real, and not illusions. Some of them were realities that appeared to exist in actual contact with the world of trees and flowers and persons; others seemed to have no direct connection with them, but they were all equally

[1] "Ode on Intimations of Immortality."—William Wordsworth.

"real", and they appeared to him with the vividness of sense-perception.

But of this world no one ever spoke to him and, if he spoke about it, people smiled or shook their heads. Sometimes in the woods he would meet a brown-robed monk, walking deep in thought. They looked as though they might have known about his "other" world, but they never spoke to him. He wished they would. So the dark-eyed little boy said nothing to others of what he saw, but to him there were always two worlds, the world which was seen by everybody, and the world which was seen only by himself. And because this other world was so vivid to him and his mind so full of its realities, the physical world around him did not seem in comparison so real, and its images did not so readily stay in his mind. They never overlaid or dimmed the realities of that other world.

Meanwhile, of all the questions in his mind this one grew to be the most insistent and perplexing. "What had this other world which he alone saw to do with the world which he and everybody else saw?" It became the question of his life. It took him forty years to find the full answer to it and he then spent the rest of his life and all his energies in trying to convey that answer to his fellow-men.

His greatest perplexity was that there was no one who could explain to him that other world. But for all that, he loved to live in it. When he was eight years old something happened which gave him the first clue to his questioning. In the room of his favourite teacher at the village school he found and borrowed a book on Geometry. All his spare time for weeks was given to reading it: he immersed himself in the axioms, constructions and problems of Euclid. But most of all was the book a discovery to him, because here was a world of forms and patterns that were drawn from the mind itself, a world in which one could live within oneself, quite apart from the outside world. Moreover, here at last was an inner world which he could share with other people. It seemed to him a link with his own private "unseen" world. It made him feel happier and more at home in it.

In the next two years other happenings added to his new-found comfort. His teacher introduced him to his own hobbies of music and drawing, and here again he found a real inner activity. Then, one day, the village priest gathered round him the older children and explained to them the principles of astronomy, the movements of sun and moon and planets. Here was another achievement of knowledge wrought by man out of his thinking. Rudolf also became a server at the village Mass, and the language and music which conveyed that mystery of the Unseen, seemed to him to corroborate the reality of that other world in which he so largely dwelt.

Lastly, the doctor from the nearby town of Wiener-Neustadt, waiting for his train at Neudörfl, would walk up and down the platform with the eagerly-listening boy, and talk about the great writers of German literature, Lessing, Goethe, Schiller. Young Rudolf drank it all in greedily. His new-found inner world of thought was growing every day. Already the world which thought brought to him seemed as if it might be the bridge between his two worlds of sense and spirit. So he passed from childhood into the life of school.

Having decided that his son's career should be that of a railway civil engineer, Rudolf's father chose for him the Real-Schule (Modern School) in preference to the Gymnasium (Classical School). The school was at Wiener-Neustadt, a town about three miles from Neudörfl. The first two years were difficult for the little boy. Although it was perceived that he was an exceptional child, yet the limitations of the village school, coupled with his own absorbing spirit-consciousness, had left him backward in such things as writing and spelling. Reading to him was a rapid assimilation of ideas without much attention to the details of language, and the crudity of the village patois added to his difficulties. Moreover, there was a long walk home each day, in winter-time across fields often deep in snow, and then there were home duties waiting to be done. But his eager zest to master the world of thought drove him on and by the end of his second year he was marked as a good scholar.

Like most boys of his age, his instinctive desire was to find one of his teachers whom he could accept as an ideal of manhood, and in such a relationship to his science master he plunged with enthusiasm into mathematics and physics and geometrical design. Still his secret world governed his striving. "My thought," he said to himself, "will never solve for me the riddles of my spirit perception, until it has reached the level at which it can penetrate to the realities behind the world of Nature."

His last years at school, from fifteen to seventeen, showed a rich development. The greatest formative force in that development arose from a happening as important for him as his discovery of the Geometry book in his village school. When he was fifteen years old he saw an advertisement in a bookshop window of Kant's *Critique of Pure Reason*, and as soon as he could scrape together the price of the book, he bought it. Of the author and his place in history he knew nothing, but the book opened a door into that world of thought, which he already felt was the key to his two worlds of Nature and Spirit. It was a step to the mastery of thinking. Amidst all the claims of home and school there was little time for a boy to master so profound a work, but so great was his eagerness that he took apart the sections of the book and placed them inside a history text-book, that he might study them during some lessons which he found dull and ineffective. In his mind three conclusions formed themselves as to the nature of thought.

1. Each thought must aim at the standard of complete accuracy.
2. There must be a harmony between the conclusions of thought and those of religion. This did not arise from any orthodox convictions, but because in his spirit-perception he apprehended directly some of the realities that were the subject-matter of religion.
3. Nothing can be excluded from the realm and range of thought. As he remarks in his autobiography, he did not realise at that time how in this point he was at complete variance with Kant. His conclusion arose directly out of his own experience.

Besides this philosophical study and the claims of his ordinary school work, there were other activities of mind and body that leave one surprised that they did not overtax the strength of his boyish years. That they did not do so was an indication of the vast range of intellectual activity which marked his whole life, and which was undoubtedly part of the result of the "wholeness" of knowledge which spirit-perception must bring. At the age of fifteen financial considerations made it necessary for him to take up coaching, and it was a tribute to his ability that even at that age his teachers were ready to commit other boys to his tutoring; some of them boys of his own year. This task of teaching others sharpened the edge of his own learning and developed in him an interest in pedagogy that played a great part in his life. But the needs of his pupils drove him to subjects outside his own curriculum, and before long he had privately mastered the classical subjects of the Gymnasium course. He also taught himself shorthand and had mastered a great part of the subjects of higher mathematics before he met them in his ordinary school work. Even for all this he had not the whole day for his studies, for his daily journeying took up three hours, and at his home he shared with his brother and sister the cultivation of their father's smallholding.

One special relationship brought a gracious and cultured influence into his school life. From his fifteenth year the doctor, who used to talk to him in his childhood days on the Neudörfl railway station, often invited him into his library at his house in Wiener-Neustadt and not only talked to him about German literature, but gave him books to read.

By the time Rudolf Steiner was leaving school three convictions had formed themselves in his mind. In the first place he was convinced of the absolute reality of the world of spirit, the world that lay behind and beyond the fields of sense-experience. Of this he had direct and continuous evidence. Although he was living at the time of the most complacent materialistic certainty in the intellectual outlook of mankind, he knew that its triumphant conclusions were false. He knew it by direct experience.

Secondly he was convinced by experience that there were no barriers to the range of thought. Religion and Philosophy both set barriers to thought. Beyond the realm of sense-experience, they said, thought cannot reach. Beyond were the realms of faith or speculation. Science on the other hand held that all that was real could be reached by sense-conscious, logical thinking, and that beyond its range there was nothing to discover. Out of his direct experience Steiner knew that both these points of view were wrong. For the world of spirit was present to his observation, and he had found that it was directly linked with the world of pure thought. When, however, thought sought to apprehend spirit realities, a thinking was involved, of a higher order than could be reached by mere logic, and one that was dependent upon a higher stage of human consciousness. In fact he already perceived *that the discovery of all truth was only a matter of ever-higher forms of consciousness, and that the way to this new range of consciousness lay open to mankind—through a deeper understanding of the nature of thought.*

Finally, he perceived that the only sound method of arriving at the truth is the scientific method of the careful and honest observation of facts, and not that of speculation. He could see only too clearly the false conclusions and fatally mistaken conceptions of the nature of Reality which could arise, when religion went beyond revealed truth, or philosophy beyond the limits of verifiable thought. Even science itself, in its theories of the Universe, was already beginning to indulge in speculation beyond observable fact. This was even more dangerous to mankind because of the guileless trust which men were beginning to place in science. Again and again Steiner had direct experience of facts which disproved these accepted speculations. For himself, then, he determined to adhere to the true scientific principle of proceeding from observable fact, and in his search for knowledge, whether of Nature or Spirit, always to wait until reality revealed itself to a rightly-developing consciousness.

All this attitude to thinking and to truth Steiner had to keep to himself, for to speak about it was only to meet with incomprehension or ridicule. This brought to him a loneliness which increased through all the earlier years of his life, as he penetrated more deeply into spiritual knowledge and experience. Until he was forty years old he experienced no sympathy in his spiritual understanding. But this loneliness was surely providentially ordered. His spirit-perceptions were not dissipated by premature discussions, nor were they led into false paths of conjecture. They remained as a matter of constant experience, and in so far as they evolved, they evolved out of his ever-developing consciousness. His opinions were not "set". He came to realise that spirit knowledge is a matter of revelation, dependent upon the will of the spirit world, and that his part was to listen, and to be ready, intellectually, morally, and with warmth of feeling, to apprehend what was given to him. In this way he was ready for new discoveries, when they came to him, and ready too to wait until their significance matured, and until he could speak or write of them in a truly scientific manner.

CHAPTER IV

VIENNA—UNIVERSITY YEARS

IN Rudolf Steiner's eighteenth year his father was transferred to a station in the neighbourhood of Vienna, in order that his son might be able to attend the Technical University there. Rudolf had decided upon the career of a schoolmaster, and enrolled himself for the subjects of mathematics, natural history and chemistry. From the point of view of his professors and fellow-students he was a successful and popular student, who took his examinations without any difficulty and who attended lectures in many branches of knowledge outside his own subjects.

At the same time he was in no sense an intellectual recluse. After his lonely childhood his mind was eager for companionship, and he found time for close and varied friendships. Two points in his character perplexed his fellow-students—and even his professors. Behind his words and arguments there seemed to them to lurk some conviction of an invisible reality, which was unreal to themselves and foreign to the intellectual spirit of the age. He hardly ever spoke of these things and never intruded them into his debates, but sometimes they were apparent in what he said. To his hearers these ideas were quite incomprehensible and they explained them in various ways, as vague mysticism, or strange philosophical hypotheses, or as the unaccountable fantasies of youth. But Steiner never forced this side of his mind upon them and it never interfered with his friendships.

The other quality in his character which perplexed—and even annoyed—his friends was his innate instinct for seeing all sides of a question. He could enter most enthusiastically into one aspect of a subject, and yet he could sympathise with and understand the opposite point of view, even when he did not at all agree with its conclusions. When he was nominated for the Presidency of the University Reading Club, he was easily elected because each party felt that he sympathised with their point of view, but in a few months his popularity waned, because he was never an uncompromising opponent of any party. On more than one occasion during his life this quality in Steiner created deep misunderstanding between himself and his closest friends, who could only see in the comprehension of an opposite point of view a betrayal of his own professed ideals. But deeply as he felt these estrangements, Steiner was never false to the honesty of his scientific approach and to the wider vision which his spiritual viewpoint brought to him.

Yet Steiner's career, as his professors and fellow-students saw it, was only the surface of a ceaseless inner struggle, a struggle to relate his worlds of spirit- and sense-experience. This can only be understood in the light of his own self-revelation. He presents in startlingly direct language the facts of his experience as he entered the University.

> Spirit and nature were present before my soul in their absolute contrast. There existed, for me, a world of spiritual beings. That the ego, which itself is spirit, lives in a world of spirits was for me a matter of direct perception.

Through all his University years, he declared, the sheer reality of this perception was the sheet anchor of his soul against a materialistic interpretation of the Universe.

Between the two worlds of his experience, however, a gulf still remained. He had formerly striven to build a bridge across it, from the world of sense-perception to the spirit-world; "but," he declared, "Nature would not pass over into the spirit-world of my experience." He now tried to build it in the other direction, from his spirit-consciousness of the ego. In the months between leaving school and entering the University he steeped himself in philosophy, Kant, Lessing, and Hegel, and that study went on side by side with his official scientific classes all through his University years. He soon found that philosophy, as taught and accepted, could not bridge his gulf, and he began tentatively to fashion his own "theory of knowledge". Could it be, he asked himself, that thoughts—ideas—were the means by which the realities of the spirit-world expressed themselves in ordinary human consciousness?

But Steiner determined to be prudent in coming to any conclusion and he never allowed his spiritual questionings to disturb his study of accepted scientific and philosophical theories. This reticence was increased by the fact that he could find no one with whom he could share his mental problems. On the few occasions when the vividness of his spirit-experience moved him to speak or write of it to others, he still found that "no one would pay any attention to it". Fortunately this spiritual loneliness was relieved by a friendship which sprang up between himself and a country herbalist, a man of no schooling, but of deep piety and direct spirit-experience.

In his first term at Vienna Steiner attended a course of lectures on German literature by Professor Karl Schröer. In this way he came into contact with two of the great formative influences of his life, Schröer himself and Goethe, to whose writings and thoughts Schröer introduced him. In an age which was turning against Goethe's idealism and had lost almost all understanding of his spiritual vision, Schröer was his unwavering disciple, and very soon Steiner had completely caught his teacher's enthusiasm. As yet the interest was purely literary and idealistic, for Schröer had no concern with, and Steiner no knowledge of, Goethe's scientific writings, which later on were to shed great illumination on Steiner's problems.

Meanwhile his own scientific studies soon confronted him with two difficulties. The teaching of biology at that time was steeped in the Darwinian theory of Evolution, and yet Steiner's direct perception of the human ego as a spirit-being was a factual contradiction of the theory that man had evolved from the lowest forms of organic matter. In physics, too, the mechanical theory of heat and the wave-theory of light made all human perceptions merely subjective physical experiences, dictated by the response of the different sense-organs to external movements. Such theories could never account for the spirit-realities of which Steiner was aware in the external world, and, however intellectually attractive the theories might appear, they denied the clearly-perceived facts of his spiritual perception. Here, again, it was not subtle cleverness nor abstract criticism that raised these objections in Steiner's mind; it was the hard fact of his lifelong experience of the spiritual. His difficulties did not drive him to scepticism in regard to science, but to a deeper study of the problem of cognition and to a clear examination of the facts of physics and biology. The conviction was strong in him, that to honest and unprejudiced examination the phenomena of Nature would reveal the answer to this apparent contradiction.

In his search for a deeper understanding of the problem of knowledge Steiner found a new clue in reading Schiller's letters on Aesthetics. Schiller postulated a "state of consciousness", in which the soul lives in sense-experience, but imports into it, unconsciously, an element of thought, a spirit-reality, which lifts sense-experience to aesthetic experience. Might it not be possible, Steiner felt, that a still higher state of consciousness would lift the soul to direct *intellectual* experience of the spiritual world? In that case philosophy and science had no right to declare as an impassable limit to human knowledge, what was only the limit that could be reached by ordinary human consciousness. Was not the truer aim to seek a way to a higher state of consciousness? Already in his own experience he had evidence of such a higher state, for he perceived clearly that the consciousness, by which he was aware of spirit-reality, was of a different kind from that by which he apprehended the sense world. In ordinary human consciousness thought is an after-reflection upon experience and stands apart from it, but in his spirit-consciousness thought and experience were united and were only two aspects of one activity. Thought sprang into consciousness at the same instant as the experience itself, as though the subject of the experience was one with the thing experienced and knew it, not only by observation, but, as it were, from the inside. To experience a thing was to know it, and the knowledge was itself part of the experience. Could it be possible, Steiner asked himself, to advance directly from the level of ordinary consciousness to this higher state of consciousness?

His problem appeared to him therefore, more and more clearly, to be a matter of a new approach to the activity of thinking. In ordinary consciousness, thinking was regarded as a faculty in man, whereby he was better able to classify and understand the realities of the physical world. To the actual activity of thinking itself men gave little attention; it was merely an instrument to lead them to the sense-realities it illuminated, and to the relationships it could derive from them. But Steiner had discovered that if he regarded the act of thinking as an activity in itself, and if he dwelt upon and lived in thoughts, in ideas, as realities which he could experience as objectively as the realities of sense-experience, this "living in thoughts" passed into that direct experience of spirit-reality, in which thought and experience were one. He felt that the bridge between his two worlds was beginning to be constructed.

Meanwhile his scientific studies presented him with a new line of approach to his problem. We have already referred to his attitude to the wave-theory of light. A deeper study of the science of optics now led him to a conclusion contrary to the teaching of recognised science, viz. that though light is a reality which plays an overwhelming part in the phenomena of the physical world, yet it is itself not perceivable by the senses. It manifests itself on physical objects in the appearance of colours, but it is itself invisible. It appears therefore to be an object of a "sensible-supersensible" kind. It stands between ordinary sense-perceptible objects and supersensible reality, manifesting itself in its relation to the physical, but itself unperceivable by the physical senses.

When he spoke of this to Professor Schröer, the latter pointed out to him the similarity between his ideas and

Goethe's theory of colour, in which Goethe had disputed the generally-accepted theory of Newton. Through this door Steiner entered upon his life-study of Goethe's writings on natural science. But he was in no way ready to accept Goethe's theory, until he had tested his own ideas by experiment, and, although the means provided by his tutoring were very small, he set up apparatus which enabled him to test further his own and Goethe's ideas. From this he was led to make similar studies in anatomy and physiology, and as a result of these he arrived independently at Goethe's theory of metamorphosis, that is, the transformation of a lower physical form into a higher one, by the working into it of a supersensible reality.

By means of this concept of metamorphosis, Steiner began to arrive at a link between physical man and the spirit-reality of his higher self, of which he was so constantly aware. He perceived that, by its activity in the soul in willing, feeling and thinking, the higher ego of man expressed itself, in ascending degrees of physical manifestation, in the human form. It was not until thirty more years of thought and spiritual perception had developed these ideas, that he revealed them to the world.

Meanwhile Steiner determined to make a thorough study of Goethe's scientific writings, in order to set out completely, in some one branch of science, the ideas which had revealed themselves to him. He had now completed his degree course and was able to pursue his studies more independently, but only by the assiduous toil of coaching in a wide variety of subjects. In all of these he had to know and teach the accepted scientific theories of the day, with no reference to his own ideas.

In 1884 an important event took place in his life. He was taken as a resident tutor into a Jewish business family of father and mother and four boys, with whom he lived on terms of the most intimate friendship until he left Vienna six years later. It was his first experience of the background of a cultured home, and on their holidays together in the Austrian Alps he shared for the first time the recreations of young people. His chief task in this home was the entire education of the youngest child of the family, a backward boy of ten, who could hardly read or write and had scarcely any capacity for sustained mental effort. To this task Steiner brought, not only his long experience of tutoring, but the full powers of his supersensible perception. He perceived the boy's spirit to be perfectly capable of intellectual development, if his soul-life could be roused from the sleepy detachment from his physical faculties in which it was held. Here was a practical opportunity to apply the theory of the metamorphosis of the physical organism by spirit-activity. He established an intimate soul-relationship with his young pupil, and thereby gradually changed his defective soul-outlook. In two years the boy had completed his preparatory school work, and was able to go to a public school, through the whole course of which Steiner guided him before he himself left Vienna. In later years Steiner had the joy of knowing that his pupil had qualified as a doctor. This experience formed the deepest link between Steiner and the boy's mother, in whom he found a spiritual sympathy and understanding he had never known before. It also laid the foundation of two of his great life-achievements, his new approach to education, and his unique treatment of the mentally-abnormal child.

Another important event in 1884 was that, on the recommendation of Schröer, Steiner was invited to edit and write an introduction to Goethe's scientific writings, for an edition of the German Classics. It was a great tribute to Steiner's scholarship and to the originality of his articles on Goethe, that at the age of twenty-three he should have been asked to undertake a work of such importance, that would extend over several years. This appointment and his resident tutorship enabled him to give up the greater part of the outside coaching on which he had depended for his living, and gave him a great deal more time for independent study.

The next few years of his life were rich in the wide variety of his personal friendships in the most intellectual and artistic circles of Vienna. The account of these friendships and of the impression they left upon his spiritually-perceptive mind, forms a most fascinating element in his autobiography. Amongst his friends were many who voiced that pessimism of life which was arising in Europe, a pessimism which saw in the indifference of Nature to good and evil and to human happiness, which the new science revealed, a denial of any permanent reality in human ideals. This pessimism was tinged with sadness, but also with a deep scorn, and later it found its fullest expression in Nietzsche. It was especially opposed to Goethe, with his belief both in man and nature, and, though Schröer had introduced Steiner to this circle, Schröer himself soon withdrew from it. This was one of the instances where Steiner's scientific impartiality wounded the susceptibilities of his friends. While, like Schröer, he was a disciple of Goethe, he realised that Goethe's concept of nature required some measure of spiritual perception, and that, from the purely material viewpoint, the pessimistic concept of nature was realistic. But this, he maintained, need not involve a pessimistic attitude towards human ideals. In an article entitled *Nature and Our Ideals* (which was the seed of his later work on cognition) he maintained that this apparent indifference of Nature existed, in order to drive man to find freedom and the fulfilment of his ideals in the triumph of his own will over Nature, both within and without him. Neither side was convinced. Schröer could only see a disloyalty to Goethe's faith in Nature, while the pessimists, among whom were some distinguished Roman Catholic ecclesiastics, held that Steiner attributed to Goethe qualities which were not to be found in him.

Meanwhile he was welcomed in both circles, but it was in complete isolation that he pursued in Goethe's writings the solution of his own problems. More and more, as he studied the scientific writings, he realised the impotence of recognised physical science to explain anything beyond the inorganic. Goethe became for him "the Galileo of the organic". Only on the lines of Goethe's concept of spiritual metamorphosis, he felt, could "life" be understood. This conviction led him to study closely the principles which govern Goethe's perception of thinking, and in 1886 he published a book on *Goethe's Theory of Cognition.* It was plain to him, however, that the point which Goethe had reached did not complete the bridge which he himself was seeking between the world of Nature and the world of spirit. He would have to work out his own theory of cognition, but he felt that it would grow out of Goethe's viewpoint.

Meanwhile, his consciousness of the spirit-world was becoming deeper and clearer, and the spirit-life of his fellow-men was becoming more and more apparent to him. An instance of this occurred in regard to the father of one of his college friends. Although he was a frequent visitor at his friend's home and was on terms of intimate friendship with him and his sisters, he never met their widowed father, who lived the life of a complete recluse. Yet, so closely was Steiner in touch with the spirit-life of this man whom he had never seen, that after his death his children asked him to give the funeral address on their father, and declared that he had given an exact portrayal of him.

In his autobiography Steiner reveals that he and the younger daughter of this house fell deeply in love with each other, but, owing to the limited resources of the young scholar, their love was never able to pass beyond the stage of intellectual and spiritual intimacy.

In all these ways many strands of rich human experience were being woven into Steiner's ripening personality. There were contacts, too, with the wider world. For a short while he undertook the editing of *The German Weekly*, but here again his scientific fairmindedness did not lend itself to the partisanship of publicity, and his newspaper adventure was a short one. But already it had brought him into touch with political and social parties, which led him to the study of Marx and Engels. It filled him, he wrote, with sadness and dismay, as he realised that those who were striving to solve the political and intellectual problems of the day, could never find any lasting solutions because of their complete unawareness of spirit-reality. Most of all he shuddered to think that high social ideals were wedded in Marxism with a completely fallacious materialistic philosophy. More and more Steiner came to feel that in Western civilisation there were spirit forces deeply inimical to the spiritual destiny of man, and even at that time he foresaw the disasters which the gospel of dialectical materialism would bring on Europe. At this time too he made his first acquaintance with the theosophical movement of Madame Blavatsky, and although he was himself becoming more and more convinced through direct spirit-perception of the truth of many of the spiritual facts which Theosophy revealed, he felt no attraction to the Theosophical Movement. He felt that its whole approach to the world of spirit was quite different from his own.

In 1888 Steiner received an invitation which gave the highest recognition to the quality of his scholarship. Some years before, the grandson of Goethe had bequeathed to the Grand Duchess Sophie of Saxony all the poet's manuscripts, and she had founded at Weimar the Goethe Archives, with the purpose of producing a new edition of Goethe's works, in the light of the study of his unpublished manuscripts. For this purpose she had enlisted the co-operation of the most distinguished Goethe scholars in Germany and Austria, and Steiner, in view of the quality and originality of his publications in the Kurschner Edition, was invited to collaborate in this Weimar Edition by making himself responsible for preparing part of the writings of Goethe which were concerned with Natural Science. In his autobiography Steiner remarks upon the fact that in this first period of his life, which lasted until the end of his task at Weimar in 1897, his work had arisen out of the inner development of his own mind, and had been in the nature of an intellectual and spiritual self-expression, unfettered by the financial necessity of accepting an uncongenial occupation.

Although he was not to take up his new post for some time, Steiner was asked to pay an immediate visit to Weimar to survey the ground and take preliminary steps. He describes the spiritual exhilaration which this visit brought to him, not only in the contacts it provided with the leading social and cultural personalities in Germany, but most of all in finding himself in the native haunts of Goethe, and engaged in investigating original thoughts and writings of his, which had not as yet been given to the world. His first eager quest was to see whether the conclusions about Goethe's methods of cognition, to which he had been led by the study of his published works, were borne out by the unpublished manuscripts. He soon discovered, to his great joy, that the manuscripts not only confirmed his views, but provided him with fresh evidence.

He took the opportunity of this visit to extend it to Munich and Berlin, where he spent most of his time in getting a first-hand acquaintance with the great art treasures of Germany, in this way strengthening by experience his conception of the relation between aesthetic principles and the knowledge of spirit-reality.

An important incident occurred to him during his visit to Berlin. He managed to secure an interview with Eduard von Hartmann, one of the leading philosophers of Germany. Steiner's short account of that interview is a dramatic illustration of his own relation to the scientific thought of his day. The massive figure of the world-famous philosopher reclined on his couch as on a throne, voicing as unquestionable his certainty that the knowledge of "the real" was buried in man's impenetrable "Unconscious", for ever beyond the reach of his abstract concepts. When Steiner ventured the suggestion —which had already become for him a certainty of spirit-perception—that concepts might after all not be entirely abstract and unreal, but might be a reflection of a spirit-reality behind them, Hartmann, with an Olympian gesture, brushed aside this "impossible fantasy". "By their very definition," he declared, "concepts must for ever remain unreal." "When I received such an answer," writes Steiner, "I was chilled to the soul. Must the understanding of the meaning of life depend upon a definition? I realised how far removed I was from contemporary philosophy. It was something which affected me for a long time afterwards."

Two years elapsed before Steiner finally left Vienna to take up his post in Weimar. They were happy tranquil years, in the congenial atmosphere of the family with whom he lived, and in the continuous study of Goethe's writings. In this study Steiner grew to see more and more clearly the relation in which he stood in regard to Goethe. Goethe's scientific conclusions were based on an intense meditation on the phenomena of Nature. He refused to be content with theories, but returned again and again to a deeper and closer penetration into the facts of Nature. He did not arrive at his key ideas about Nature by a process of abstract reasoning, but, in his concentrated observation, the ideas arose in his mind as mental pictures. Steiner perceived that these were really images of the spirit-realities behind Nature, but that Goethe took no further step towards them, lest he should lose himself in abstractions. Instead, he turned back again to the phenomena of Nature, in the light of his inspired perceptions.

In his exposition of Goethe's world-outlook Steiner knew that he was expressing something that was implicit in Goethe's writings, but of which Goethe himself was not wholly conscious. It fell to him to complete Goethe's revelation by working out his own theory of knowledge, based on his own direct perception of the spiritual. To this task he devoted his thought during these two years.

Steiner realised that it was a great act of destiny that had brought him into this relationship with Goethe. His study of Goethe had certainly ratified his own first tentative approach to the problem of reality, but it had also involved him in an intellectual task, which inevitably slowed up his own spiritual development. At the same time it steadied and controlled it, and, as we shall see, eventually opened up a rich avenue of approach to the problem from the side of physical phenomena, which would not have come naturally to Steiner.

Another question which Steiner faced at this time was his relation to traditional mysticism. While he shared with the mystics their concern with spirit-reality, in the matter of approach they took completely opposite views from his own. Most of them regarded thought as opposed to spirit, and rejected it as a road to spirit-experience. In its place they adopted the path of feeling, and sought spiritual reality only in inward experience. Steiner knew that, without the corrective of clear thinking, inward experience can easily be subjective or pathological. Moreover, by denying the applicability of thought to spirit-reality, the mystics played into the hands of the materialists. For they limited the range of knowledge to sense-phenomena, and left the direct experience and understanding of spiritual reality to temperamental subjectivity. So opposed was this to Steiner's whole attitude to thought, that he determined that he would never employ the language of mysticism to describe spirit-reality and experience, but would find forms of expression that were parallel to those used in regard to natural-scientific reality.

Just before he left for Weimar, Steiner took his doctorate in philosophy at Rostock University. His chief regret on leaving Vienna, was the severing of the deep spiritual relationship which existed between himself and the mother of the children to whom for the past years he had been tutor.

CHAPTER V

WEIMAR DAYS—THE GOETHE ARCHIVES

When Rudolf Steiner moved to Weimar in 1890, his work at the Goethe Archives brought him into a more public life than he had known at Vienna. Artists, writers and scholars of the first rank, not only in Germany but in Europe, lived in and visited the city. The Goethe Institute, as the creation of the Grand Duchess, was one of the most important elements in its cultural life, and Steiner, as one of the official collaborators, was at the heart of this life and in constant touch with all these personalities. In addition to the writers and artists, he was brought into touch with the Court circle of Weimar and with people of the highest rank in Germany. In all these varied contacts Steiner felt that he was being forced into contact with the outer world in a quite new way, and he realised afresh how shadowy for him the sense-world had always been, and how much more at home he was in the world of spirit.

In his work at the Institute he found two opposite approaches to Goethe, one that was more concerned with the creative, spiritual side of the poet's mind and work, and the other which approached it as a problem of psychology, philology, and comparative literary form and classification. With the first point of view he was in natural sympathy, and he was fortunate in that two of his chief colleagues took this approach. But, to his disappointment, the other point of view became more and more general.

We have already spoken of the difficulties and misunderstandings into which Steiner was led by his capacity for sympathy with and understanding of those with whose ultimate conclusions he was completely at variance. This occurred at Weimar in regard to two most distinguished relationships into which he was drawn. The first was with Haeckel, whose scientific studies on the lines of Darwinian evolution had made him famous, and whose philosophy of evolution was arousing a storm of interest and opposition. Steiner's admiration for his scientific methods of observation and for the fact that he used observable facts alone as a basis for his thinking, was wrongly interpreted as an endorsement of his materialistic philosophy, with which Steiner profoundly disagreed.

An even more complicated situation arose in regard to his relation to the poet Nietzsche. That historic figure, which in a few years had blazed its path across German and European thought, was already struck down by blindness and mental sickness. But his writings, with their convention-shattering violence, had created mutually hostile camps of friends and foes. Since he had first read his writings in 1889, Steiner had been struck by the depth and freshness of his feeling, by the fiery intensity of his spirit, and by the penetrating accuracy of some of his denunciations. He wrote a book on his work entitled, *Nietzsche as the Adversary of his Age*, as a result of which Nietzsche's sister invited him to undertake the task of setting in order the sick poet's library. This brought him into touch with Nietzsche's official editor and gave him the reputation of being a Nietzschean. Yet all the while Steiner was aware that this tormented spirit, in spite of the brilliance and perception of so many of his aphorisms, had lost his way as a thinker. He saw in him a being of great depth and insight and fearlessness of spirit, whose inspiration and true spiritual destiny had been frustrated, because his mind had completely accepted, and was imprisoned within, the materialistic scientific world-outlook of his age. When Frau Förster-Nietzsche paid Steiner the great compliment of inviting him to share in the further responsibility of editing the poet's works, he had to give a refusal which he knew would create an irreparable breach in their friendship, and in that of many who regarded him as an avowed admirer of Nietzsche. It seemed impossible to explain that he could sympathise with and admire the spirit and utterances of one, with whose conclusions and philosophy of life he was completely at variance.

In his domestic life at Weimar Steiner's life fell on happy lines, as it had done at Vienna. In his second year he obtained rooms and board with a Frau Eunicke and her children, and lived with them on terms of intimate friendship during the rest of his stay at Weimar. Frau Eunicke's husband, who had died shortly before she had met Steiner, had been a scientifically-minded man, who had found it impossible to accept a spiritual explanation of the universe, but had lived the simple life of a recluse. Although Steiner only knew him through his widow and because he had the use of his study and books, nevertheless he was able, as he had been in the case of the father of his college friend at Vienna, to follow his life clearly into the spirit-world. In his autobiography Steiner remarks quite simply that it is, of course, open to anyone to refuse to believe in the reality of these spirit experiences. Nevertheless, he declares that he investigated them with the same exactitude and objectivity that he gave to the study of mathematics. He found, in this case as he had done in the other, that the spirit-life of the man concerned was little affected by his earthly inability to form a spiritual concept of the world. Indeed, he perceived that his capacity for judgment had become enhanced by his scientific mentality. It became clear to him therefore, that it was only when a materialistic world-concept became expressed in the *will*, in a materialistic way of living, that it became a danger to future well-being in the spirit-world.

This perception was not only a matter of personal interest, but it brought an enlightenment and clarification of ideas to Steiner's mind, which determined the final form of the book, *The Philosophy of Spiritual Activity*,[1] which he published in 1894, and which expressed the result of many years wrestling with the problem of knowledge, and of the relation between the worlds of sense and spirit. This book was a landmark in the evolution of Steiner's spirit-consciousness, and there are some points in regard to it that we must grasp, if we would understand its relation to that evolution.

The book is not a philosophy in the ordinary meaning of

[1] The German title is *The Philosophy of Freedom.*

that word. It is entirely based on Steiner's actual experience that pure thought led him directly into the realm of spirit-reality, in which were manifest to him the relation between thinking and sense-perception, and between conscience and conduct.

But nothing of this experience is directly expressed in the book, and it does not deal at all with the objective realities of the spirit-world, which are the constant theme of Steiner's later works. It is an attempt to lead the reader, by logical and clear thinking, from the universal level of sense-experience and sense-derived knowledge, to a deeper understanding of the nature of thinking as a true spiritual activity, and of conscience as a real participation in objective moral fact; and of the conscious exercise of both of them as leading to the goal of human freedom.

Steiner sent a copy of the book to Eduard von Hartmann, and it was returned with copious comments and detailed criticism. Steiner writes in his autobiography, "He had utterly misunderstood the sources of my ideas—and the aim of my book."

By 1897 Steiner had completed his examination and arrangement of Goethe's scientific writings and his work at Weimar came to an end. In his last year a new development took place in his consciousness. He himself calls it "a profound revolution". We have already noted how much more at home Steiner was in the spirit-world and how comparatively difficult he had always found it to concentrate on the physical realities of the world of sense-experience. Suddenly he experienced a complete change. He describes it vividly in his autobiography:

> An attentiveness—not previously present—to that which appeals to sense-perception now awakened in me. I had the feeling that the sense-world had something to reveal, which it alone could reveal. I came to think that one's aim should be to learn to know this world, solely through that which it had to say . . . I was given an entirely new world.

This change in his consciousness was partly due to the

fact that meditation, which had been for Steiner the pathway to his understanding of the spirit-world, had become more and more a necessary part of his daily life. There can also be little doubt that Steiner's study of Goethe's scientific works over the previous years contributed largely to the awakening of this new experience. As we have already noted, Goethe arrived at his intuitive perception of the spiritual realities present in nature, solely by an intensive meditation upon the phenomena of Nature. In his investigation of Goethe's scientific writings, Steiner followed him in his spiritual-scientific approach to the world of sense, until at length his own wider powers of spirit-perception became able to take the same path, and to pursue it much further. In deep and concentrated meditation upon the facts of sense-experience, Steiner's consciousness began to break through to the spirit-realities behind the world of minerals, plants, animals, and men, in a knowledge in which his whole being —thought, feeling and will—participated.

There were now for him three types of knowledge. In the first place there was the ordinary intellectual apprehension of the sense-world. Then there was the direct apprehension of spirit-realities experienced inwardly in pure thinking, a knowledge that transcended thought, but arose out of it. Now there was this new knowledge of the spirit-realities expressed in the sense-world, derived from direct meditation on sense-phenomena.

This new knowledge was not arrived at out of penetrating logical thought; indeed, in the meditation through which it was reached, every activity of mind and body had to be stilled. It was as if one sat silently before the facts of the world of sense-experience, until the eyes of the spirit were opened to their secrets. And yet the meditation was of the nature of thought. It was not a logical activity, that analysed the sense-phenomenon in order to arrive at the mechanism of its physical being, or the ultimate rudiments of its material substance. It was a concentration upon the phenomenon as it is manifest to the senses, *in its complete form*, in an endeavour to penetrate to the ideal realities of form or colour or growth or consciousness, expressed in it. It was a concentration that demanded the awareness of the whole being of the observer, his feeling and will no less than his thinking, and it awoke in him deeper faculties of perception. It was still *thought* that was leading him on to the world of spirit, but in the process thought itself was transformed into a higher form of perception. This was a knowledge which led to wider fields of spirit discovery than Steiner had ever reached before. Each object of sense-experience became a doorway into the world of spirit, not only manifest in the visible phenomenon, but actively at work in it, informing and upholding it.

This new method of penetrating into the reality of the universe, revealed all the more clearly to Steiner the fundamental error in the then widely-accepted atomistic method of natural-scientific investigation. Both natural and spiritual science were based on an intensive study of sense-phenomena, but the natural scientist relied too much upon logical analysis and experimental hypothesis. Having accumulated all the evidence offered by the perception of his physical sense, and having reduced it, by logical analysis, to its ultimate component elements, he concluded that the task of observation was now over, and proceeded to fashion, out of his observation and analysis, a hypothetical explanation or world-picture based on that evidence. In most cases the world-picture transcended the evidence, and propounded as realities what were only thought-fantasies. The answers to all these riddles, Steiner perceived, was not to be found in thought-speculation, but in the phenomena themselves. They could, however, only be discovered by this concentrated meditative thinking, and in that sense man himself holds the key to the secrets of nature. In such concentrated meditation, human thinking is brought into awareness of the creative activity of thought that lies behind the world of Nature.

More and more clearly could Steiner see that the error of the natural-scientific world-outlook was entirely bound up with *its false idea of matter.*

The scientist [he writes], contemplates matter as complete in itself, without being aware that he is in the presence of spirit-reality, manifesting itself in material form. He does not know that spirit metamorphoses itself into matter, in order to attain to ways of working which are possible only in this metamorphosis. For example, spirit expresses itself through a material brain, in order that man may, by that process of conceptual knowledge, attain to free self-consciousness. By means of the brain man derives spirit out of matter, *but the instrument he uses is itself the creation of spirit.*

The deeper Steiner penetrated into direct experience of the spirit-realities expressed in the world, the wider seemed the gulf which separated him from the thought of his day. It seemed impossible to bridge it. It appeared to him as though all the forces of darkness were massed against the revelation of the spirit. In face of them he felt that he could no longer remain silent about the truths, of which he was aware.

Meanwhile his work at Weimar was over and for the first time in his life he was faced with the problem of choosing his career. For some time he had felt that through the medium of a paper he might be able to convey something of his spiritual message. In 1897 he accepted the offer of the editorship of a magazine, which took him from Weimar to Berlin.

CHAPTER VI

BERLIN—SPIRIT INITIATION

THE next five years in Steiner's life were intensely critical. His life-long search for the connection between his natural clairvoyance and the world of sense-perception had found its first clue in pure thought, and its second in concentrated meditation on the phenomena of the physical world. As yet these bridges were not sufficiently strong or secure for him to pass at will between the world of sense and the world of spirit with fully conscious understanding of their relationship, but he felt that he stood on the very threshold of discovery, and that his whole thinking was permeated with new powers of perception. He felt a burning desire to impart his knowledge to his fellow-men, enmeshed as they were in scientific materialism. But to do so directly was impossible; no one would listen to him. He could only speak through the activities which he could share with others, and these were conditioned by the necessity of earning a living.

The *Literary Magazine*, of which he became the Editor, concerned itself with the latest literary expressions of the intellectual life of the day in Germany and other countries. It was a long-established, independent weekly, but it had identified itself with the Free Literary Society, which represented the younger and more revolutionary literary circles of Berlin. They were a band of aesthetically-minded and somewhat self-conscious persons, and the articles had to be such as would appeal to this clientele and also to his co-editor, a man of very different calibre to himself. This was all the more necessary, as the financial position of the magazine was very insecure and was entirely dependent upon its subscribers. For the first time in his life Steiner found himself attached to a circle, which was temperamentally and spiritually unsympathetic to his own nature.

The activities of the Free Literary Society involved him in lectures, dramatic productions and dramatic criticism, in addition to his editorial work, and in all he wrote and said he endeavoured to present his theme as he saw it from the point of view of his spiritual knowledge, while keeping it within the vocabulary and experience of his hearers and readers. It was tedious and difficult work and brought little evident result, and it was inevitable that articles should appear in the magazine with which Steiner was not wholly in sympathy. It was an unfair criticism that in after years held up some of these articles as evidence of inconsistency in his outlook. What is much more remarkable is to discover the many passages in which, in the light of his subsequent teaching, it is plain that he was trying to enable spirit-truth to break through the materialism of his readers. On the other hand, the necessity for delivering his message through the medium of writing, lecturing and play-production, enabled him later, in the full development of his spiritual knowledge, to invest these activities with a new technique of understanding and performance.

Sometimes Steiner wondered whether he was justified in pursuing a course in which his real aim and purpose had to be concealed; he was therefore all the more conscientious in devoting himself with all his powers to his task as editor and secretary of the Society. Fortunately, his private circumstances soon became settled and peaceful, for a few months after his arrival in Berlin the Eunicke family moved there from Weimar and he immediately joined them. Not long afterwards he married Frau Eunicke.

It was fortunate that he had this stability at the centre of his life, for those closing years of the century were critical to him, and produced a much deeper and more shattering conflict than the difficult and somewhat equivocal nature of his outer activities. Here again we penetrate into a realm of experience which most people have never entered, nor even realised that it exists, and it is only through Steiner's own autobiography that it could have been revealed. But in the spiritual evolution of his consciousness, which is the real theme of this sketch of his life, the spiritual crisis of these years was vital. Steiner speaks so earnestly and definitely about it in his autobiography, that his words carry conviction.

In the midst of all his public activities, he never abandoned his consistent effort to penetrate more deeply into supersensible reality. It was in profound and concentrated meditation on pure thought that he had made his first discovery of the links between the two worlds, and such meditation became more and more a daily necessity. Now his meditations extended to the facts of Nature, over which he pondered in a purely scientific spirit of concentrated observation. But here we touch a fact that is fundamental to the understanding of the search for spirit-reality. In observing the phenomena of the physical world by the methods of natural science, the student seeks to remain absolutely detached from the object of his observation and to regard it impersonally. But in the spirit-world, to know is to experience, and to experience is to know. Concentrated meditation upon a spirit-reality becomes at length a fusion of one's being with it, a fusion which involves, not only thought, but will and feeling. Thereby one enters into a quite new and incomparable reality of perception and knowledge, but, unless the whole personality is held in balance and in clear consciousness, there is also the risk of being overwhelmed by this intense experience.

Moreover, as Steiner penetrated into the supersensible reality behind physical phenomena, he became aware, not only of objects, but of spirit-beings and their working. In fact, the whole universe revealed itself to him, as permeated through and through by spirit-activity. As he himself expressed it, "The spirit world is not a sphere of relationships between beings and objects, but between beings and beings—and objects always as the expression of beings."

In his meditative endeavour to arrive at the perception of spirit, and to combat the mechanistic-materialistic form of scientific thinking, Steiner found himself in contact with spiritual beings, whose one aim, he perceived, was that man should acquire this very materialistic outlook, and that the world should more and more come to be regarded as a machine.[1] Behind the materialistic world-thought of the day was their deliberate activity. To an age which has lost almost any belief in the existence of spirit-beings, the idea of spirit-beings consciously influencing the trend of human thought and activity will at first appear incredible. On the other hand, there are an increasing number of persons, other than Steiner, who have had similar experiences, and nothing can exceed the simple directness with which Steiner relates his experience and how deeply it affected him. No longer was it for him merely human error and delusion that hindered the realisation of the spirit basis of reality; it was a spirit-hostility that was far more terrible to overcome, *because it could only be overcome by entering into the experience of it.* "At that time," he writes, "I had to save my spiritual perception by inner battles."

Fortunately there was another direction of spirit-experience that was opening for him at this time. One of the results of his developing spirit-faculties was that he entered into a different form of Time-experience, in which past events can be recovered, with the same validity and immediacy as any present physical experience. Clearly in such an experience there is an entirely new possibility of historical research and understanding, and on no field of knowledge, as we shall see, has Steiner thrown more light. At this point we will not attempt to explain this experience, but merely record it as an event in Steiner's life.[2]

In this experience of the past he came face to face with the facts of Christianity, spiritual as well as historical, and he gave himself with great earnestness and wonder to the study of them. It was his salvation against the fierce onset of the evil Ahrimanic powers. He writes:

> In this time of testing I succeeded in advancing farther, only when in spiritual perception I brought before my soul

[1] These are the spirit beings whom Steiner designates as "Ahrimanic". see p. 104.

[2] For an explanation of this experience, see pp. 84 and 99.

> the evolution of Christianity . . . After the time of testing had set before me stern battles of the soul, I had to submerge myself in Christianity, and in the world in which the spiritual speaks thereof.

This fact is all the more remarkable, because, in his articles in the magazine at that time, he wrote critically and disparagingly about Christianity. This was, later, one of the chief lines of attack on the reality of his Christian convictions. But it was the formal, organised Christianity of his day that Steiner criticised; not the content of its faith, but its refusal to allow to thought the possibility of penetrating to the understanding of the higher truths of the Christian revelation, and the insistence that these could only be grasped by a faith strictly regimented by formal theology. Moreover he attacked formal Christianity, because for it the spiritual world was always regarded as something quite "other than" and "future to" the physical.

Although he had been brought up in a "free-thinking" home, yet in his childhood Steiner had felt the presence of spirit in sacramental worship, and he had always believed that true knowledge would be in harmony with religion; indeed, it was just these experiences of religion that made him critical of the attitude of organised religion. In his newly-achieved direct evidence of the historical facts of Christianity, its inner content began more and more to unfold within his soul. It was not with him a matter of doctrine, it was a reality of spiritual experience with which he was increasingly confronted. Especially did he ponder in deepest wonder and reverence before the central mystery of Golgotha, the passion and death and resurrection of Jesus Christ. As the century drew to its close, the great crisis of his struggle with the spirit-forces of materialism passed into the light of Christian certainty and understanding. "The evolution of my soul," he wrote, "rested upon the fact that I stood before the mystery of Golgotha in a most inward, most solemn festival of knowledge."

As with St. Paul before him, it was a spiritual vision and

certainty which became the mainspring of his whole life. In all his thinking, he was thenceforth completely Christocentric. The Incarnation he could see as the pivotal fact in all history, human and divine, and the deed of Christ on Golgotha, not as an article of faith, but as a mystical fact that interpreted all history before it, and affected every department of earthly life and history after it.

Meanwhile Steiner was becoming widely known as a lecturer and he was invited to lecture on history to the Berlin Workers School. It was a new experience for him to be teaching adult men and women of the working class. The dominant thought of the school was Marxism, which was stronger at that time in Germany than anywhere else, but the Committee agreed that Steiner should be entirely free to lecture according to his own views of history and human evolution. As always, Steiner strove to understand his hearers by penetrating into their soul-life, and he describes how impressed he was by their intense craving for knowledge and how tragic it was that only gross materialism had troubled to offer them a form of expression which they could understand. For under the conditions under which they had been forced to live, economic forces were a factor of which they had immediate experience. Starting from the undeniable truth of the powerful working of economic forces in history since the sixteenth century, Steiner was able to lead them to recognise the real effectiveness in history of religious, artistic and moral motives. His lectures were popular and he was asked to give the festival address at a vast meeting of type-setters and printers in Berlin.

Gradually the leaders of the Workers' School became aware that his teaching contradicted the wholesale materialism of the Marxian world-outlook, and a movement was started to get rid of him, despite his popularity. One of the lesser leaders voiced the Marxian point of view with prophetic exactitude: "We do not wish freedom in the proletarian movement; we wish rational compulsion." The opposition became so intense, that, after four years in this work, Steiner was forced to give it up.

Meanwhile, with the growth of his lecturing, he was able in 1900 to give up the editorship of the magazine. He had now determined that he would try to express more directly his esoteric knowledge. He had already made one or two attempts, in an article in the magazine and in a public lecture, to give some indication of the esoteric nature of some of Goethe's writings, when he received an invitation from the Count and Countess Brockdorff to lecture at one of their weekly gatherings. For the first time he found himself addressing an audience most of whom were keenly interested in the spiritual world. The Count and Countess were members of a branch of the Theosophical Society and many of the audience were Theosophists. When he received a second invitation, Steiner gave a lecture that was fully and unqualifiedly esoteric. Immediately he received an invitation to lecture regularly. He made it plain that he was not himself a member of the Theosophical Society, and that he could and would speak only out of his own direct esoteric experience. The invitation was renewed on those terms. In this way he began his life-task of openly calling mankind from scientific materialism and philosophic agnosticism, to an experience and understanding of the spirit background of human life, in which lay both the origin and destiny of mankind. From this task he never desisted until he laid it down in death twenty-three years later.

CHAPTER VII

SPIRITUAL SCIENCE AND THEOSOPHY

RUDOLF STEINER'S work of spreading the knowledge of spiritual science fell into three stages. The first twelve years of the century were spent in the development of his own esoteric knowledge and in imparting and expounding it. The next six years were spent in laying the foundation of a movement which would ensure that his work would go on after his death. In the last six years of his life—post-war years of intense political and social crisis—he was actively engaged in applying spiritual science to all kinds of human activity.

In his autobiography Steiner reveals that the first ten years of the century were a time when the facts and being of the spirit-world came more and more intimately into his direct experience. By regular, concentrated meditation his powers of spirit-perception developed, through the stages which he describes as Imagination, Inspiration and Intuition. This whole process and the full significance of these names will be developed in a later chapter, but they signify three successive and ever-higher stages of spiritual consciousness. The first stage gives knowledge of the spiritual background of our physical life and of the world in which we live. The second stage opens the way into the purely supersensible world, giving understanding of its conditions and of the beings who inhabit it, and of their relation to the physical world. The third stage is one in which a man is able to act himself as an inhabitant of the spiritual world, and to have intercourse with those to be found in it.

The knowledge derived from these levels of higher consciousness falls into three categories: the knowledge of the supersensible nature and significance of the physical phenomena that are the field of inquiry of Natural Science; the knowledge of the inter-relation of the physical and spiritual in the being of man, both in his earthly existence and in the spirit-world; and finally the recovery of the whole past of mankind, reaching back into ages far behind human history or even earthly existence.[1] The development of these categories of knowledge is manifest in the books which Steiner produced in the first years of the century, *How to obtain knowledge of the Higher Worlds*, and *Theosophy*; the latter a specific account of man's earthly and spiritual existences and the relationship between them. Although the subject-matter is unfamiliar and not easy to grasp at once, one cannot fail to notice the factual way in which it is presented. The two books which he had produced previously point to the importance to him of the Christian revelation which had come to him at the turn of the century. These were *Mysticism in Relation to the Modern World-Conception* and *Christianity as Mystical Fact*. To these were added a few years later his remarkable courses of lectures on the four Gospels and on the Apocalypse.

In the Theosophical circles of Berlin Steiner met, for the first time, people who were not only willing, but anxious, to hear his spiritual message. From 1900 to 1902 he lectured to them in an entirely independent manner, and his lectures made so strong an appeal that his audiences rapidly increased. One of those attracted to his lectures was Marie von Sievers, a woman of great intellectual and artistic power. Almost immediately she and Rudolf Steiner were drawn into a close friendship, and they collaborated most effectively in all his subsequent life-work. In 1914 she became his second wife.

In 1902, in response to this growing interest, the headquarters of the Theosophical Society in London decided to form a German Section of the Theosophical Society at Berlin, and asked Steiner to accept the position of leader. At first he refused. He had come into touch, some years before, with the teaching of the Theosophical Society and had not felt in sympathy with it, partly because of a tendency in some of its leaders towards mediumistic spiritualism, and partly

[1] For an explanation of this, see pp. 97 ff.

because it was more concerned with the study of the ancient mystic teaching of the East, than with realising in man today the faculties of direct supersensible knowledge which the present stage in the evolution of humanity demanded and had made possible. However, with urgent pressure, both from Germany and London, he finally accepted the position, but only upon the explicit assurance that each Section of the Theosophical Society was completely independent in the management of its own affairs, and that he himself should be free to speak, as he had been doing, out of his own direct spirit-experience. Not only were the conditions granted, but Steiner was given a warm welcome by the Theosophical leaders in London. His consent was not only due to the pressure of his friends. He felt that the awakening of Theosophical knowledge, and the discovery of the spiritual treasures of the East in the early part of the nineteenth century, had been a spiritual counter to the rapidly-growing scientific materialism, and that the Theosophical Society had been founded out of a genuine spiritual impulse and experience. He hoped to be able to help it to return to that which he conceived to be its true task in European civilisation. Moreover, although he already had non-theosophical audiences, he felt that in Theosophists there was an existing life of spirit, into which he could more fruitfully sow the seed of a new spiritual world-outlook.

The years that followed were a giving out, ever more deeply and through ever-widening circles, of the knowledge of the facts of the spirit-world, in relation to man's being and to the origin and evolution of the physical world. Out of his continually-deepening experience of the spiritual there awoke in Steiner knowledge on all sorts of subjects, which carried him far beyond the levels attainable by ordinary scientific methods. In imparting this knowledge, he always adhered to the principle that he would only impart supersensible facts which he had himself directly observed, and only when he had tested them by frequent observation and by relating them, by careful thought, to other known facts. He never merely recounted his spiritual experiences, nor would he build conjectural theories upon them. He often warned his listeners of the dangers of doing this and told them that one should be silent about the significance of a spiritual precept until, by repeated observation, the spiritual facts themselves revealed it.

Steiner's fame as a lecturer spread rapidly and other Theosophical centres sprang up in Germany, at Munich, Stuttgart, and other places. Invitations also arrived which took him to most of the countries of Europe. To look through a list of his engagements during those years makes it appear almost incredible that any one person could have delivered so many lectures, on so many and varied subjects, all of them in relation to the spiritual background of life. Although Steiner adapted himself conscientiously to the accustomed phraseology of the Theosophical Movement and to the general programme of its teaching, from the first the German Section had a spiritual vision and originality that were derived from its leader's ever-increasing spiritual knowledge. It was the certainty and originality of his message that created the demand for his lectures in every part of Europe.

In an account of a lecture-cycle, given by special invitation at Paris in 1906, Edouard Schuré, the great French authority on the ancient Mysteries, gives a vivid picture of the unique effect which Steiner had on his audiences.

> When Rudolf Steiner [he writes], was describing the events and realities of the spirit-world, he seemed to be absolutely at home with them. He was not describing, he was actually seeing the objects and scenes of these unknown regions, and he made them so visible to others that cosmic phenomena appeared actual. Listening to him, one could not doubt the reality of his spiritual vision, which appeared as clear as physical sight, but with a far more extended range. I would have crossed the Atlantic to hear him.

Gradually it became plain that the new wine could not be contained in the old bottles. The points of difference between the teaching of Rudolf Steiner and the official outlook of Theosophy sharpened into a fundamental opposition.

The first point was the divergence between the approach to spiritual knowledge in the East and in the West, between Indian Theosophy and Western occultism. The leaders of the Theosophical Society were identifying themselves more and more with Indian mysticism, accepting its vast cosmogony of the spirit-world—the origin and destiny of man and the nature of his pre-earthly and post-earthly existence—and were relying entirely, for any direct understanding of this, upon the Eastern methods of training for clairvoyance, by a complete withdrawal from physical phenomena and a retreat into man's own inner being.

Steiner knew, of course, of the Eastern esoteric methods and appreciated them as the right methods for a past stage in human evolution. But he declared them to be quite unsuited to the mind and make-up of the Western world and to the spiritual task to which at that moment it was being urgently called. One of the great secrets of history to which Steiner had penetrated by his supersensible development was the scarcely known fact that, while the ancient Eastern mysteries had played the greatest part in the evolution of humanity and had left behind them a profound literature, there had been in Europe an ancient mystery-knowledge, which had been preserved in its primitive simplicity, until it met the new wave of human evolution which swept over Europe with the spread of Christianity. This esotericism, which from time to time manifested itself in many streams of European thought and culture, came to its most precise form in the Rosicrucian esotericism of the fourteenth century, since which time it had remained completely occult and in the knowledge of very few individuals.

During the first three years of his connection with Theosophy, Steiner gave very many lectures tracing this esoteric stream in the thinkers and mystics of Europe. It was so opposed to the Eastern esotericism to which official Theosophy was more and more committing itself, that eventually the Society leaders actually denied the existence of any primitive European esoteric sources. Now the point of opposition between

Eastern and Western esotericism lay in their attitude to the physical world, and it was precisely in the attitude of Western esotericism that Steiner saw its applicability to the evolution of the West, and also the impossibility of building a true spiritual science on Eastern mysticism. For Western esotericism had always sought to find the mystery of the spirit, not in isolation from the physical world, but where it lay hidden in the material objects themselves in whose forms it manifested itself, and it strove with all its might to penetrate to direct apprehension of this spirit-reality behind the physical. Indeed it was out of the pursuit of this search in alchemy that the modern scientific approach to matter originated.

This Western esotericism, therefore, Steiner saw to be in direct relation to the modern scientific spirit, in spite of the avowed materialism of modern science and its rejection of any reality beyond the range of sense-perception. He had, of course, discovered for himself the relationship between scientific thinking and spiritual knowledge, in his lifelong effort to reconcile his own consciousness of both worlds. In doing this, he had perceived that the moment had arrived when what had formerly been occult knowledge must now become open scientific teaching. Science had reached the stage when, if it would but overcome its prejudices, it could penetrate to the direct knowledge of the supersensible. In a note to Edouard Schuré in 1907 Steiner set forth the three provisional explanations of world-phenomena, in arriving at which science had made possible this new stage in the evolution of human consciousness. These were,

1. The new understanding of the heavenly bodies by spectral analysis;
2. The introduction of the principle of evolution into the understanding of organic life;
3. The recognition through hypnotism and the study of the Unconscious of other levels of human consciousness than the physical.

This concentration on Western occultism brought Steiner

into an attitude towards scientific thought which again was quite foreign to official Theosophy. The latter was not interested in the scientific approach to spirit knowledge and regarded it with suspicion. Steiner, on the other hand, approached spiritual knowledge as a scientist—indeed he called it "Spiritual Science". He maintained that it was not sufficient today to reveal the facts of spirit-reality by recounting the great spiritual teachings of the past, but that the time had come when man should begin to advance to direct knowledge of the supersensible world, by developing his own latent faculties of spiritual perception, in full rational consciousness. He declared that the development, in the last three centuries, of logical thinking and of the scientific spirit of observation, had been a necessary step in human evolution, towards man's re-discovery, at a higher level, of the spirit background of the universe. His only quarrel with Science was that it accepted the limitation of scientific observation to the phenomena of sense-existence, and that, in forming its world-concepts, it regarded the atomistic bases of matter, rather than the significant forms of physical objects, seen in relation to their environment and their particular metamorphoses, as the key to ultimate knowledge, and took refuge in theoretical world-concepts, unverifiable by direct observation. He regarded it as fundamental that spiritual knowledge should be justified before the scientific way of thought. As we have seen, he had himself discovered that pure thought, if it were exercised from the point of view of its own intrinsic worth, was the means whereby man could reach a level of consciousness, which would give him a knowledge of supersensible reality as verifiable to reason as any other fact of Science. Moreover it would confirm the vast cosmogonies of the ancient world in a way that was no longer possible to ancient methods of initiation. The Theosophical attitude to Science was to look away from it and above it. Steiner's attitude was to identify himself with it, in a determined effort to set it free from its self-imposed limitations and errors, and to lead it into new fields of knowledge. Thus the entering into spiritual knowledge *in the mode of scientific thought* was to Steiner the essential path of modern esotericism, but to official Theosophy it was not only unknown, but suspect.

The other vital difference between Steiner and official Theosophy was in regard to his conception of Christianity in relation to other religions. With his interpretation of the past as the story of the spiritual evolution of the human consciousness, Steiner saw the great religions of the East as profound revelations, arising out of and conditioned by the stage in the spiritual evolution of humanity at which they came into being. But in the Christ-event he saw a unique divine deed, the fulfilment of the dim prescience and the intense longing of the ancient religions, and the fulcrum of the whole spiritual history of the human race. This was distasteful to the Theosophic conception of the equality of all religions, as varying manifestations of the same Spirit, and more than once it was pointed out to Steiner that his attitude would cause offence to Eastern Theosophists. Steiner, however, insisted that this was a matter of spiritual truth that admitted of no concession to expediency. He also pointed out that, before he had joined the Theosophical Society in 1902, he had given a series of public lectures entitled *From Buddha to Christ* in which these views were clearly expressed, and that in his book *Christianity as Mystical Fact*, published in 1902, he had carried them even further.

In some ways it may be felt to be unfortunate that Rudolf Steiner ever had any connection with the Theosophical Society, for the eventual break led to a great deal of ill-feeling and recrimination on the part of Theosophists. Moreover, in later years it enabled other detractors to identify him with many of the vagaries of the Theosophical Society, and to deny the originality of his spiritual experience. At the same time, nothing could have brought into such sharp outline the exact nature of Rudolf Steiner's world-outlook and of the scientific and fully-conscious paths to higher knowledge taught in Anthroposophy, than that, in loyalty to them, he should have parted company with a worldwide spiritual movement in which he held a position of international influence. It should be noted clearly that it was on the ground of the uniqueness of the revelation and deed of Christ, and the relevance of science and the faculty of rational thought to the present stage of the spiritual evolution of humanity, that Steiner was forced to dissociate himself from the Theosophical Society.

Owing to the constitutional independence of the national sections of the Society, it was only at the biennial congresses that the tension became manifest. It first appeared in 1907 when the congress was held at Munich and it fell to the German Section to arrange it. With his deep conviction that this new era of the spirit should express itself, not only in lectures and discussions, but in every form of artistic and creative representation, Steiner had the great Concert Hall at Munich decorated in form and colour designed to harmonise with the general mood of the programme. For the first time, a dramatic representation was given of an arrangement by Steiner and Marie von Sievers of Schuré's reconstruction of the Eleusinian drama. The older members from other countries were displeased at these innovations, but, at this stage, Annie Besant supported the right of the German Section to independent action. Two years later, when the Congress met at Budapest, the gap had widened. Two distinct and opposed voices of Theosophy were heard, Mrs. Besant extolling Buddha over Christ, and Rudolf Steiner describing Buddha as the mighty announcer of Christ, who was himself the centre-point of earthly evolution. Still there was no open breach, though mutterings of the approaching storm could be heard.

In 1910 the final rift developed. Mrs. Besant, now living in India, announced that in Krishnamurti, an Indian boy, the Christ would be reincarnated, and she presented him as such to a great assembly in India. An order, entitled "The Star of the East", was formed to promote the acceptance of this "revelation" in all the Sections of the Theosophical Society. Steiner absolutely refused to allow a branch to be formed in the German Section. Immediately a storm of abuse and defamation from the older members broke on his head. Undeterred, he carried on with an arranged tour of conferences through the countries of Europe, and announced, as the theme of his contribution to the approaching Theosophical Congress at Genoa in 1911, *From Buddha to Christ.* When he was actually on his way to Genoa, he received a bare message that the Congress had been arbitrarily countermanded. His challenge was avoided. Immediately he gave his proposed lectures, and followed them up with a most penetrating cycle, *From Jesus to Christ*, in which he indirectly answered some defamations that had been circulated about him.

Meanwhile, recognising the imminent parting of the ways, Steiner's own followers urged him to reply openly to the attacks on himself and his teaching, but this he declined to do. At the end of 1912 a meeting was held with the intention of forming an independent body within the Society, under the name "Anthroposophy", that should dissociate itself from the oriental party. This Steiner followed with yet another cycle of lectures on *The Bhagavad-Gita and the Letters of St. Paul*, showing once more how in Christ the two streams of East and West could meet.

Suddenly in January, 1913, Mrs. Besant wrote an official letter intimating that Rudolf Steiner was no longer recognised as leader of the German Section. On February 3 the first General Assembly of the Anthroposophical Society took place.

CHAPTER VIII

THE ANTHROPOSOPHICAL SOCIETY

EXCEPT in name and constitution, there was nothing new about the Anthroposophical Society. It was a direct continuance of the work and teaching of Rudolf Steiner since 1900, and of the life of the German Section[1] of the Theosophical Society. The name itself Steiner had used frequently in his teaching. Of course his enemies derided him for having forsaken the wisdom of God for the wisdom of Man, but the word Anthroposophy has no significance of that kind. Various definitions of it are given and perhaps no one definition would contain its whole meaning. The word "sophia" always denotes the divine wisdom, and "Anthroposophy" indicates that this wisdom is to be found in the knowledge of the true being of man and of his relation to the universe. There is also the further connotation that, whereas formerly the divine wisdom was imparted by the divine world itself to man, now man himself, by divine grace, must transmute his earth-born thinking to the higher level of divine wisdom, by the true understanding of himself.

The Society was formed, not merely as an association of Steiner's supporters, but as a living movement of the spirit, which sought to awaken in mankind new powers of spiritual perception, and also to apply, to all departments of human life and thought, the spiritual outlook and understanding which had been given by Rudolf Steiner out of his own supersensory perception. Thus the Anthroposophical Society has never been a mere "cult", existing for the esoteric development of its members, but a movement seeking, in practical ways, to lead mankind into a new spiritual understanding of man and the universe.

[1] The German section included Austria and the German-speaking part of Switzerland.

At its foundation, the membership of the Society already included leading men in all walks of life, academic, professional, and industrial, all of them seeking a new level of spirit life in their own calling. Nor was it contained within the limits of the German Section of the Theosophical Society, for its members were drawn from all the national Sections of Europe. Besides these, there was an increasingly large number who had had no connection with Theosophy.

In 1910 Rudolf Steiner had brought the whole of his supersensible understanding of the evolution of the Universe and Man into one volume, under the title *An Outline of Occult Science.* In the same year he wrote *The Portal of Initiation,* the first of a series of four modern mystery plays, written one by one in subsequent years. These plays represented the process of Initiation to Higher Knowledge among a group of people in modern life. The plays were produced year by year at the annual meeting of the German Section, a very important part of the teaching of Rudolf Steiner. When the Anthroposophical Society was formed, there was felt the need of a central building in which these mystery plays could be adequately produced, and which should also be the centre of anthroposophic research and activity in all directions of human interest. Moreover, the building itself was to represent in its architecture and the artistic form of its interior construction and decoration, the principles of metamorphosis and of the other relationships between the spiritual and material worlds, revealed by Spiritual Science.

An attempt was first made to find a site in Munich, but, on opposition from the authorities, Steiner accepted an offered site in Switzerland, on the slopes of the hills outside the village of Dornach near Basle.

Future events have proved how beneficent was the destiny that centred the Society in this neutral country. The proposed building was a vast financial undertaking for a Society with only a few thousand adherents, but it was greeted enthusiastically. Money and offers of service flowed in from most of the countries of Europe, and the foundation stone was laid in September, 1913. A year later the main building was erected, but even before it was finished, the cataclysm of the first world war broke over Europe. It almost seemed as though the full forces of the powers of evil had determined to crush the bursting flower of this new spiritual growth. For it was plain that a European war would release forces of violence that depended upon and would utilise the material forces of science, and would tend to establish scientific and political materialism. Such forces would have no consideration for the calmness and universality of spirit, necessary for spiritual knowledge.

Rudolf Steiner saw all this, but he continued steadfastly in his work. His European activities were no longer possible, but he concentrated on the building of the "Goetheanum"—as it was to be called. All the painting, wood-carving and glass-engraving still remained to be done, and it said much for the spirit of the Society, that men and women from all the warring nations worked hard together at this task. All through the war Steiner continued to lecture in Germany, speaking much on the great problems of life and death, and on the spiritual destiny of his own people, and the true understanding of the great leaders and thinkers of its past. His lectures were entirely free from pan-Germanism, though he foretold only too accurately the failure of the Wilsonian resettlement of Europe, with its sacrifice of human economic interests to the spirit of a separatist nationalism. Also, when the Russian revolution established itself under Lenin in 1917, he foretold at once the disastrous consequences which history has already confirmed.

With the coming of peace and the social upheavals consequent in Europe, Rudolf Steiner came forward with an entirely new approach to social and political problems, based on the three-fold nature of Man. His book *The Threefold Social Order*, published in April, 1919, created a great impression in Germany and was soon translated into many languages. It made a great appeal to manufacturers and workers, and his lectures had crowded and tense audiences. Then opposition arose, on the one hand from the Communists and trade union parties because the movement stood outside their party programme, and on the other hand from the Junkers and the parties of reaction. But it was the newly-arising National-Socialist movement that finally closed the door in Steiner's face. At a crowded meeting in 1922 their violence prevented a hearing, and Steiner's life was threatened. His agents refused to take the risk of booking further engagements for him, and so, after twenty-one years of unbroken activity, his lectures in Germany came to an end.

Undeterred, Steiner took up his work in Dornach, and devoted himself to extending the application of Anthroposophy in other directions. Already in 1920, under his guidance and direction, the Free Waldorf School in Stuttgart had been opened by Herr Emil Molt, a manufacturer of that town, primarily for the education of the children of his factory-workers. It grew rapidly and became the model for a wide-spread system of education on the Anthroposophical lines of the spiritual individuality and importance of every human being. In 1920 the Gotheanum was sufficiently completed to inaugurate it as "The Free University of Spiritual Science and the new Science of Man", and to hold in it the first "Anthroposophical University Course" which was attended by six hundred registered students and a large number of the general public. Courses of lectures, confined to doctors and medical students, were also given, which resulted in the founding of special research institutes and clinics; and there were also lectures on agriculture to farmers, on education to teachers, and on religion to theological students. Meanwhile, besides these activities, there were developed, in the light of Spiritual Science, all forms of art and of dramatic representation, particularly in connection with the Mystery Plays. There was also evolved the new art of movement called "Eurhythmy", which had been devised by Rudolf Steiner and developed by Marie von Sievers (now Marie Steiner).[1] Eurhythmy is an art which expresses in movement the same spiritual forces which are expressed in speech and music. Although as an art it is yet in its beginning, Steiner reveals that in its full development it will be the expression of a level of spiritual evolution,

[1] See Chapter XIV, p. 162.

towards which humanity is moving, but which still lies far ahead. Already it has proved to be of great curative and educational value.

In the face of all this intense activity the forces of opposition grew, not only from political parties and trade unions, but from theologians and scientists; but at the same time the membership of the Society increased in every country. Suddenly a great disaster occurred. On the night of December 31st, 1922, fire broke out in the Goetheanum.[1] As all the building, with the exception of the cement substructure, was made of wood, it was impossible to check the fire, though by heroic efforts some of the most valuable contents were saved. As Steiner and his fellow-workers watched helplessly the fruit of so much sacrifice and devotion, and the creative expression of the great spiritual secrets of man and the universe for which they stood, consumed in a few hours of roaring conflagration, they felt that all the opposing forces of evil and materialism were massed, to overwhelm their message of light and spirit. But though he almost felt that he himself was consumed in that holocaust of his hopes and dreams, the spirit of Rudolf Steiner was undaunted. The work must go on, and steps were immediately taken to obtain temporary accommodation, and plans were set on foot to build the Goetheanum anew.

Meanwhile Steiner could feel the intense strain which his ceaseless spiritual and physical activity had imposed upon him, and in the remaining two years of his life he concentrated his efforts upon strengthening the spiritual life of the Movement, and in seeking to equip to the full those who should follow him. He also re-expressed, for educated, but uninformed, audiences, the fundamental principles of Anthroposophy and of the paths to Higher Knowledge, which he had laid down in his early books twenty years before, and he did this in terms of the most direct scientific thought, which all could follow.

At Christmas, 1923, he refounded the Society, with a new

[1] It was the official verdict of the fire-authorities that the cause of the fire was incendiarism.

constitution on a universal basis. In 1924 he established an esoteric class, in which he sought to train an inner circle of members in the attainment of higher knowledge.[1] Towards the end of this year he was taken seriously ill and was confined to his bed, but from his pen, in the form of articles and letters to the members, he sent forth a continuous stream of spiritual teaching and inspiration.

In these last years too, as a factual and non-contentious answer to attack and criticisms, he set forth what he describes simply as *The Story of My Life*. He was not able to complete it. On March 30th, 1925, he died.

Such was the life of the man who was the sole teacher and founder of Anthroposophy, and whose direct supersensible experience is the only immediate source of much of its teaching. As we have said and as the examination of the teaching itself will make clear, the ability to accept and be convinced of its truth does not depend on the ability to share that supersensible experience. But the object of this account of his life has been to show the consistent, steadily-progressing evolution of Rudolf Steiner's inner consciousness, and its entire devotion to critical judgment and to scientific and dispassionate thinking. Nearly thirty years have passed since his death, and the confusion and frenzy of those years—affecting, as they have, even the minds of those to whom it has fallen to carry on his work—have done much to conceal from mankind the significance and appeal of his life. But if the urgency of our times impels us to look into this teaching that appears so relevant to our need, there is nothing in the life of its author and founder that will not enhance and justify it. Indeed we cannot but feel that his clear understanding and appreciation of the need and outlook of Western civilisation, and his belief in and devotion to the spirit of scientific inquiry on which it has been based, commend his teaching to serious and unprejudiced study.

[1] Esoteric classes had been given in earlier years, but they were now established in a more formal way in relation to the Society.

CHAPTER IX

NEW HORIZONS OF KNOWLEDGE

As we have already seen, the teaching of Rudolf Steiner was derived from what he declared to be his direct perception, at higher levels of consciousness, of worlds of higher reality, invisible to the organs of sense-perception. It is important therefore to begin our study of his teaching by trying to understand the nature of these higher worlds, and the methods by which direct knowledge of them is obtained.

This is all the more important, since there is a deep prejudice against the reality or desirability of such knowledge on the part of Natural Science, modern Philosophy and Religion. The whole range of Natural Science is based upon the study of phenomena perceivable by the physical senses, or derived by logical inference from such knowledge. In regard to the great problems of the origin or destiny of man, or the nature of his higher faculties, Science holds, either that the answers are to be found in material phenomena, or else that they are beyond the range of any exact knowledge. All mystic vision or spiritualistic phenomena it regards as due, either to a psychopathic condition, or to the working of subconscious physical forces.

Philosophy, on the other hand, in its work of logical philosophic speculation, accepts as its primary facts the same phenomena of sense-perception as Science, and refuses to base its speculations on any other kind of reality. The Christian religion, interpreting the realities of sense-experience and adding to them other realities in the light of revelation, has nearly always disapproved of any attempt to obtain direct knowledge of the supersensible. This is due to the fact that for the last two thousand years such knowledge was, as a rule, only obtained through spirit-possession of a low or evil kind.

Rudolf Steiner was in complete agreement with the contention that there were necessary limits to the range of a natural science that depended only upon sense-perception, and he deprecated any attempt to solve the problems of human existence by speculation of any kind, philosophical or scientific, that went beyond ascertainable facts. He also fully admitted the unreliability of any supersensible knowledge that was based upon the lowering of the self-consciousness and clear judgment of the seeker. But he claimed that Anthroposophy was entirely free from these defects. It proceeds by the entirely scientific method of the investigation of directly-perceived facts, by clear, rational judgment. The fact that the realities of the spiritual world lie outside the range of physical consciousness does not, he held, necessarily make them unattainable. It only calls for the search for higher levels of consciousness at which they can be perceived, and this he claimed to have reached in an entirely scientific way, by the development of higher faculties of perception latent in the human organism.[1]

Moreover, he felt, as we have already seen, the urgency of defeating the materialistic world-outlook, which Natural Science had evoked, and which he saw would reduce humanity to frustration, and seriously impede the true course of its spiritual evolution. In all sorts of directions, he declared, mankind is already unconsciously coming into contact with supersensible reality. If it were induced to interpret these contacts materialistically, it would place itself at the mercy of evil forces, which sought to use their own knowledge of the realities of the supersensible world for evil ends. In seeking true knowledge of higher worlds Anthroposophy is not engaged in a vain anticipation of a future existence, but in arriving at an understanding of the whole background and

[1] "Is not Science merely one mode of experience? And are we to believe that the quality of our ordinary consciousness is so fine that further states of consciousness are inconceivable? Are not further states of consciousness most likely to be the key to the understanding of the complexities and contradictions that have arisen in the realm of physics?"—*Living Time*, p. 35, by Maurice Nicoll. cf. Also the quotation from Sir James Jeans on p. 18.

significance of man's present being and of his earthly environment, in order that he may know and follow the true path of his evolution, as a being of body, soul and spirit.

What then is the nature of these higher worlds and what are the methods by which knowledge of them is attained? In the first place it is important to understand what is meant by the expression "higher worlds". These "worlds" are not separate regions, spatially divided from one another, so that it would be necessary to move in space in order to pass from one to the other. The higher worlds completely interpenetrate the lower worlds, which are fashioned and sustained by their activities. What divides them is that each world has a more limited and controlled level of consciousness than the world above it. The lower consciousness is unable to experience the life of the higher worlds and is even unaware of their existence, although it is interpenetrated by them. But if the beings of a lower world can raise their consciousness to a higher level, then that higher world becomes manifest to them, and they can be said to have passed to a higher world, although they have not moved in space.

We have a parallel to this in the physical world. There are endless levels of consciousness in it, from a mere sense of touch in the lowest forms of animal life, through all the grades of sense-awareness, up to man, who adds to sense-awareness thinking. He is in a world of which the animal is unconscious. The analogy is not complete, but it illustrates how the acquisition of new organs of perception will lift a being to a world of new experience.

It is in this sense that Steiner speaks of higher worlds and how to attain to the knowledge of them. The subject occupies many books of his teaching, and all that can be done in this introduction to his work is to give such an account as will show the relationship of these levels of supersensible consciousness to one another and to our normal physical consciousness, and the rational and fully-conscious processes by which they are attained.

We have already learnt that Steiner himself started from an innate supersensible consciousness and that, in seeking the link between that and normal sense-experience, he found it in the transformation of thought. In setting out, therefore the path which others must follow, he starts with the universal human faculty of *thought*.

We are all familiar with the power of thought to recover from the storehouse of our memory pictures of past events in our life, recalling them as they happened. It is this power of thought to form inner images that has to be developed. This is done by a process of concentrated meditation in which the whole personality, in its thought, feeling and will, is completely centred upon some object. This object in itself should not be drawn from the storehouse of memory, though the details out of which it is constructed will be familiar to experience. For if this concentrated thinking is to be an instrument of supersensible perception, its content must, as far as possible, be independent of our physical organism and experience. Our memories are tied up with past physical experience and, as memories, are subject to subconscious bodily processes, whose activities, rising into consciousness, might easily be mistaken for a genuine spirit-experience. We must choose, therefore, objects for our meditation which are independent of physical experience, as for example the processes of growth in Nature, which, as such, are not discernible by sense-perception, or objects of a symbolic kind, or some passage of Scripture, or of other mystic writing. In his books Steiner indicates many possible objects of meditation.[1]

The purpose of this meditation is, in the first place, purely the training of our thinking and the development of the powers latent in it. Everything depends on perseverance and the concentration by which all else is excluded from the mind except the object of meditation.

The time required for this development will vary with different people, but eventually, with sufficient perseverance and concentration, there will be noticed an intensification of our thought-images. We all know that if we form a thought-image of some material object, although we may recall it in

[1] As, for example the Rose-Cross, a black cross wreathed with red roses.

detail, our thought-image lacks the vividness of direct sense-perception—as we discover in a moment if we look again at the material object. Now, as a result of the meditation exercises, it will be discovered that the thought-images that arise in connection with them gradually become *as vivid as those of direct sense-perception.* A new power of thought has awoken in us. No longer are our thought-images merely a rather faded reflection of sense-experience, but our thought has developed the power to evoke, *out of its own pure activity,* the most vivid images, quite independently of sense-perception. We have developed an activity of thought that is not dependent upon our physical organism. Now this acquired faculty of sense-independent, rational thinking is one of the most important features in Rudolf Steiner's whole system of Spiritual Science, distinguishing it completely from any other form of occult or mystic knowledge and justifying his claim to describe his knowledge of spirit reality as a "Science". We shall return to this later in this chapter.

So far nothing in the nature of external, super-sensible reality has been revealed, but in the awakening of this new power of thought there develop long-dormant soul-organs of perception. These organs once functioned in primitive man in an instinctive and unselfconscious manner; but with the awakening of intellectual consciousness they have become atrophied. In the training for the development of higher knowledge they are reawakened and augmented to a higher activity, lit by the clear consciousness of the newly-acquired power of sense-independent thinking. Gradually there arises within the consciousness something else besides our thought-images. There appears a tableau of the whole of our inner life of thought, feeling and will, from the very beginning of our earthly existence. It is a well-known fact that such a tableau of the whole past life appears at times to a person, under a great shock or in imminent danger of death, but it is involuntary and only lasts for a short time.[1] In this case,

[1] cf. "One fireman carrying a burning hydrogen cylinder, liable to explode at any moment, said afterwards, 'The whole of my twenty-five years with the service passed before me as I carried it'."—Reported in the Press of 18/5/53.

however, it is an experience which manifests itself objectively and can at any time be recovered.

This tableau is not only a recollection of the happenings of our earthly life, but the events are present to higher consciousness as actual experiences, as though they were being experienced again. In this respect we find ourselves in a new relationship to Time. Although these events happened in our physical experience separately and in succession, they now seem present to us as one unified whole. Their successive relationship has not disappeared, but they are unified into a higher entity—like separate notes of music that, sounded in a certain time-relationship, become a melody. The separate notes are still there, but, together with the time-relationship in which they were sounded, they have become a new entity which comprises them all. In this way Time, which to the seeker's physical consciousness appeared as a medium *within which* he had a succession of experiences, is now *part of his being*, welding those successive experiences into one continuous whole. He sees himself, not as a being *in* Time, but *as a Time-being*. For what he sees is not just a *picture* of the events of his past life, which he can observe with his thought from outside, as he did on earth. He realises that in this living, inter-related continuity of experience *he is beholding himself* in a higher dimension of being, of which on earth he was unconscious.

Let us pause for a moment at this point and consider whether there is anything in our physical consciousness that will enable us to form a clearer concept of this metamorphosis from "successive" to "continuous" Time-consciousness; from Time as that "within which" events happen, to Time as part of one's actual being. If we can begin to form some concept of this first step in the transformation of our consciousness, it will help us to understand the nature of the higher levels of consciousness which lie beyond it. Indeed, the understanding of the true nature of our Time-existence is the clue to the understanding of the whole teaching of Spiritual Science.

Now, our earthly experience of Time is that of Past, Present and Future. Our past experience is behind us and is irrecoverable, the future is unknown and cannot be anticipated. It is only the present moment which we can control and which we immediately experience, and therefore we come to regard reality as, for us, bound up with each present moment. The real nature of our being we see as ever changing, but only definable in terms of its qualities at each successive "present" moment.

Nevertheless, we do not conceive of our existence as a series of completely detached, momentary experiences. We think and speak of ourselves as including in our existence experiences immediately preceding the actual "present" moment. We say that we are having a happy day, or enjoying a pleasant holiday. Again we conceive of a dramatic play which it may take two hours to experience or of a symphony to which we have listened for half an hour, as something which we experience as a single event.

Moreover, the discoveries of the phenomena of the Unconscious reveal that the realities of our past experience are still related to our present being, even though they lie quite outside the range of immediately remembered experience. Indeed, very often there is no memory of having had the experience. Furthermore, when they are brought into present consciousness by means of hypnosis, they can recur, not as memories, but as an actual experience. Again, the fact that the past experience was not properly related to the doer's being, by reason of fear or shame or of some misconception in regard to it, can bring a diseased condition to his present consciousness.

Thus it appears that the whole of our past experience has a reality which survives the disappearance of the material objects and events which evoked it, and that it exists in a unity of being which is conditioned by moral and other considerations, which are not implicit in its material origin.

It would, therefore, not be an unnatural assumption to hold that the continued reality of our past experience is independent of the cessation of our material existence; in other words, that our whole earthly inner experience survives physical death and that the soul, after death, is immediately confronted by its whole earthly past, recoverable at any point, not as a mere memory, but as an actual experience.[1]

Now it is this assumption that Higher Knowledge perceives directly as spiritual fact, and we see that our physical experience and the phenomena of the Unconscious both point towards it. It is not the nature of our earthly existence, but our consciousness of it, that has been transformed. Our life is still a chain of events, but our being is not identified with the last, or the last few, of its links, but with the whole chain as a unity. Moreover, what higher knowledge perceives is what has always existed and functioned in this way, but this was unperceived at the lower level of physical consciousness.

To return to the seeker, we find that he has made a further discovery. For he perceives that the tableau presents, not only the whole sequence of his conscious earthly experience, but also something of which he has hitherto been quite unconscious, namely the working of an ordered system of inner soul-forces, which have built up and maintained the whole life of his physical being from birth onwards. He perceives also that these forces are the same as those by means of which his brain functions in thinking. He sees that in his earliest years these forces were almost exclusively employed in forming and developing his body and its organs, and that it was only after his seventh year that they were released for the activity of thinking. But he can now see how, all through his life, these forces have fashioned and sustained his physical body and its functions, interpenetrating it as an ever-mobile thought-structure, maintaining its organic life. To this structure Steiner gives the name of the "etheric body" or the "body of formative forces", or the "life-body". These formative-forces are found wherever there is life, and to those who have reached this level of consciousness, they are manifest in animals and plants, as in man.

Moreover, as the seeker traces back the time-sequence of the "tableau" of his life, he perceives that, before his physical

[1] This was the theme of the book *The Eternity of Time*, referred to in the Preface.

embryo was conceived by his parents, this etheric body already existed as the formative and creative pattern of his own individual physical being. Of one thing he is now sure; that organic life is not the product of matter, but is the constant expression of spirit, as life and form, in the medium of matter.

To this first level of higher consciousness is given the name of "Imagination", from the developed power of thought to express itself in vivid images or pictures. Great, however, as are the discoveries which are made at this higher level of consciousness, they deal only with the supersensible realities and processes at work in and behind man's own being and the physical world.

In one sense there is a fundamental difference between the etheric and the physical worlds. In the etheric world there are no static objects, nothing is at rest. It is a world of constant movement and ever-changing life, form succeeding form in ceaseless metamorphosis. Particularly is this so in the matter of physical growth and decay. In the physical world life is succeeded by death, but in the etheric world there is always manifest behind physical life the constantly-evolving pattern of spirit-life. Even though the physical form is decaying into lifeless, motionless matter, behind it is already evolving the ceaseless pattern of spirit-life arising out of it, to be manifest later in another form.

But although this life of ceaseless movement and change is clearly evident, it is difficult, at that stage, to interpret it or fully to understand it. The realities of the spirit-world itself are not yet revealed. For this a higher level of consciousness is required, and to attain it the faculties of the soul must be developed still further. The seeker has already attained the power of emptying his consciousness of sense-impressions and lifting it to the apprehension of the etheric world of formative forces working in the physical. He must now be able, by a continued process of concentrated thought-meditation, to discard from his consciousness these newly-acquired etheric-physical images and to hold the soul in conscious and expectant emptiness. Then there arises into this emptied consciousness, a world of supersensible beings and happenings.

All possibility of illusion is excluded, inasmuch as the seeker retains his newly-acquired faculty of sense-independent thought. This gives him clear consciousness and power of judgment, against which the beings and events he witnesses reveal themselves in unquestionable objectivity. Moreover, he can at any moment return from this higher consciousness to his normal physical consciousness and, once he has acquired the power of emptying his consciousness, he can do so again at will at any time or place. In this way he is able to contemplate and assess his experience of this spirit-world, and to describe it in such a way that anyone with normal healthy intelligence can follow his explanation, even if he himself has not developed any powers of supersensible perception.

This second stage of higher consciousness Steiner calls "Inspiration", because the awareness of the spirit world it evokes flows into the emptied consciousness, just as the air is breathed into the physical body. It is a world of spirit-beings, in constant inter-relationship, who continuously send forth their activity into the etheric and physical worlds. The nature and activity of the spirit-beings is expressed in the endless and varying relations in which they stand to one another, just as the letters in the alphabet, in endless groupings and in varying order, express, to those who understand the language, an infinite variety of meaning. It is only by training up to the second level of higher consciousness that the significance of these spiritual relationships can be deciphered and understood. This is called "the reading of the sacred script".

The etheric-physical world was discovered to be a world of the forces of life and growth and form. This world, which is called the "astral" world, is a world of soul-conditions, a world of desires and hopes, of fears and emotions, of attraction and repulsion. Moreover, just as the etheric forces were moulded into a "form" or "body" which interpenetrated the physical body, so the seeker can perceive that there is in his earthly organism an astral body, inter-penetrating both his etheric and physical bodies, and that it is through this astral body that he possesses consciousness, and has the experience of emotion and desire.[1] This astral vehicle of consciousness is found also in the animal world, but it is not present in the world of plants. In the animal world this consciousness and emotion work at a much more impersonal and undifferentiated level than they do in man. This is due to the fact that human consciousness is interfused with that *self*-consciousness which man alone possesses, and the nature of which he now begins to comprehend.

In this astral world, of which he has become aware, the seeker makes a most important discovery. He discovers that the real core and centre of his own being is not the self-conscious ego of his earthly existence, which he had always regarded as arising out of his physical existence in the form of his inner life of thought, feeling and will; but that it is an immortal self, whose home is in this spirit-world, from which it has descended into the physical world. He sees that it is the presence of this higher self, working through his astral body, that has awoken in him that self-consciousness which is the spur of his being, and which distinguishes him from the rest of the physical world. Nevertheless, by identifying that self too closely with his experience of the physical world, through which he has become aware of it, man has formed a distorted and false concept of himself, which almost completely obliterates his awareness of his true higher self.

Yet another feature of this astral world manifests itself to the individual who has reached this level of "Inspiration". He sees that it is a world no longer bounded by the earthly conditions of time and space, but that it is a qualitative world, where moral values have the same necessity as natural law in

[1] Constantly in his teaching about the nature of Man, Rudolf Steiner refers to the "etheric body" and the "astral body", functioning in the organism of each individual human being. There is no suggestion in the use of the word "body" of any material substance. Just as the physical elements in man are contained and expressed in a physical body of a particular shape and content, so the etheric life-forces and the astral consciousness-forces in man are also expressed in a definite form or "body", manifest to spiritual vision. These "bodies" interpenetrate the physical body, but they are more mobile. Nevertheless they are recognisable to supersensible perception in form and appearance, and it is in this sense that they are called "bodies".

the physical world. This is indicated in the fact that its whole activity consists in personal relationships. He now sees the etheric tableau of his own earth-life in a new way. Just as in "Imagination" he saw that it had all been inter-penetrated by etheric reality, so now he sees that it was also inter-penetrated by the higher astral reality. He perceives that the vital, eternal element in it consists of all the personal relationships that took place in it, and he also sees that the whole of it was inwrought by the activity of spirit-beings. His earth-life, therefore, now appears to him, not only as a time-reality, a continuum of events; but it is transmuted into a moral reality, a pattern of personal relationships, in regard to which he feels himself judged by his own higher self and by this world of spirit-beings.

The discovery in the spirit-world of his higher self leads inevitably to the impulse to rise beyond mere perception of the spirit-beings of this world, and to enter into direct and conscious relationship with them, i.e. to live oneself as a spirit-being. This, however, necessitates a still further development of the spirit-organs by an intensive training, not of thought only, but of the will. It necessitates a moral self-discipline of the highest order, particularly a release from self-centredness, and the development of a pure disinterested love of others, before the third level of higher consciousness, "Intuition", is attained. When that happens, the seeker is living as a dweller in the spirit-world, in complete union with it and in mutual inter-penetration of being. Just as in Imagination he became aware of the time-significance of his earthly life and of the spirit-forces at work in his physical being, and as in Inspiration he discovered the moral significance of his life and the true nature of his being, so in Intuition he becomes aware of the nature and range of his existence as an eternal spirit. He is able to follow the evolution of his being, through a recurrence of earthly lives alternating with a return to a spirit-existence, and he also sees clearly, how, as a consequence of his former earthly lives, the moral necessities of his whole eternal being work into each new earthly life. In other words, he becomes directly aware of the fact of Reincarnation and of what is generally given the widely-misunderstood name of "Karma". In an understanding of these lies the answer to the eternal human problem of Freedom and Necessity, but they involve so deeply the whole question of the origin and destiny of man that they must be dealt with in a separate chapter.

We have seen, then, that the path to higher knowledge set out in Anthroposophy is an ordered training of the human faculties of thought, feeling and will, to successively higher levels than that of their normal activity, in complete consciousness and clarity of judgment. We have also seen that in acquiring higher consciousness man makes a most important discovery about the nature of his earthly being. He discovers that man in his earthly organism is a four-fold being. In addition to the material substance of his physical body, he possesses three other elements of being, all inter-penetrating one another and his physical body, and each of them functioning according to the laws of its own level of existence. That which gives life and the powers of growth to the material element of his body is provided by a "body" of formative-forces, the etheric body; that which imposes controlling form on the life-forces of his etheric body, and which gives him consciousness and the capacity for feeling, is provided by a body of sentient forces, his astral body; while at the centre of all is the immortal core of his being, his ego, whose home is in the eternal spirit-world.

All this he knows, not as a theory, but as an actual discovery in the process of acquiring higher knowledge through the development of the latent spirit-faculties of his being. At each stage he becomes immediately conscious of the functioning of the new level of being, by divesting himself of the consciousness of the lower level.

In this way he makes two important discoveries. In the first place he makes the discovery that the cessation of a lower level of consciousness only means an awakening to a higher level. This gives him an assurance of life after death. This assurance is made doubly sure by his actual perception, in the recovery of his own past existence in his higher knowledge, that several times already he has entered into and passed out of a physical existence.

The other discovery that he makes is that his earthly existence consists in the functioning of his eternal ego, through the inter-penetration and inter-working of the three "bodies", astral, etheric and physical. The ego itself is most closely associated with the astral, or soul-body, the seat of consciousness, while the etheric is more closely attached to the physical body. This close association of the etheric and physical bodies is necessary for physical life and it only comes to an end with death. This is the explanation of the sudden tableau of the whole past life which has been known to arise under imminence of death from drowning or some other sudden event. It is a momentary flash of the etheric time-consciousness, partially released from the physical.

It is now plain that man's earthly being, consisting in the inter-relation of these four vitally real elements, cannot be understood either in its history, or in its true function, or in the matter of education or of bodily health, if it is regarded merely as a physical reality, and if the activity of its other elements is explained as in some way proceeding from the material physical world.

In point of fact, Rudolf Steiner sheds light on one of the most universal and familiar human experiences—namely, waking and sleeping, with the intermediate stage of dreaming —by relating it to these new levels of higher knowledge. The discovery in higher knowledge that man's being functions in three worlds—the spiritual, the astral, and the etheric-physical—reveals the fact that, in falling asleep, the human ego, together with the astral body, its proper environment, dissociates itself from the etheric and physical bodies, which remain at rest in unconsciousness—the astral body being the vehicle of physical consciousness. The necessity for sleep is seen to be due to the fact that, in waking life, the activity of thinking is dependent upon the same etheric formative-forces which build and sustain the physical organism. In this way the waking life of conscious thought causes a disintegration in the physical organism, which can only be restored by withdrawing consciousness, so that the etheric formative-forces may concentrate upon the restoration of the physical body.

On the other hand, the experience of the ego and the astral body in deep sleep remains unconscious, because they are no longer in contact with the thought-forces of the etheric body and the sense-organs of the physical body, which alone in man's physical existence stimulate the astral into consciousness. It is only when the ego has been able to develop an intensive thinking, not based in any way upon physical sense-experience, that it is able to carry consciousness into the astral sphere. This would enable it to retain consciousness in the condition of sleeping and dreaming.

While, however, Steiner has shown that the path to higher knowledge proceeds in an orderly and rational manner, by an intensification of the normal faculties of the human being, it must not be assumed that higher knowledge is merely a matter of thought-development which anyone might expect to be able to achieve. Again and again Steiner speaks of it as a very difficult path, a goal which can only be attained by constant patience and perseverance. He also reveals that on the path to higher knowledge there will be met strange and in some ways alarming experiences, as indeed might well be expected when one passes to the knowledge and experience of a completely different state of consciousness. Such experiences call for great reserves of moral courage and understanding.

We have already noted that Steiner declared that it was impossible to advance to the third stage of higher knowledge, Intuition, except after special moral preparation. But such moral preparation is a necessary preliminary to *any* attempt to seek knowledge of the higher worlds. The seeker must attain certain moral qualities before he commences his search at all, and these qualities are not those most generally possessed today. The most essential of them is a complete humility and a sense of reverence towards the whole world of reality, and particularly towards one's fellow human beings. There must also be a mood of tranquillity, a realisation of the supreme importance of the inner life of thought and meditation, and an ever-increasing control over one's faculties of thought, feeling and will. Indeed, as one reads the moral requirements which Steiner sets out as necessary conditions in this search for higher knowledge, one is deeply reminded of the moral qualities which are set before men by Christ in the Sermon on the Mount, as the necessary qualities for those who would enter into the kingdom of heaven.

So far from promising the seeker an easy path to higher knowledge, Steiner declared that "higher knowledge may be made to develop in other ways, by following certain other instructions, but that all such methods are rejected by true Spiritual Science, for they lead to the destruction of physical health and to moral ruin. They are easier to follow than those here described. The latter, though protracted and irksome, lead to the true goal and cannot but strengthen morally". "For every one step that you take in the pursuit of higher knowledge, take three steps in the perfecting of your own character."[1] Those who follow the path set out by Rudolf Steiner, even though they do not succeed in themselves attaining to the experience of higher knowledge, cannot fail to find their character strengthened and themselves better fitted to face the problems and duties of their daily life.

The other essential condition of higher knowledge in Spiritual Science is that clear, conscious thinking and rational judgment, of which we have already spoken. In his direct perception of spirit-reality and his realisation of the urgency of delivering mankind from the materialistic world-concept to which Natural Science was leading it, Steiner perceived that any knowledge of the spiritual world which could claim to be a "science" must be based upon observed spiritual facts, comprehended and related to one another and to the world of sense-perception, by the same power of rational thought which animates natural science.

It is in regard to this necessity that we stressed earlier in this chapter the fundamental importance of Steiner's development of sense-independent thinking. In the very acquisition

[1] *Knowledge of the Higher Worlds*, pp. 139 and 70.

of this new faculty, as we have seen, man finds himself raised to a higher level of consciousness in which he becomes objectively aware of supersensible phenomena, which, by the same faculty of sense-independent thought, he is able to verify, to understand, and to relate both to one another and to the world of sense. Moreover, every advance to a higher level of spirit-reality is made by a further intensification of this same power of sense-independent thought, by means of which the phenomena discovered at each stage can be rationally comprehended.

In this way Steiner was able to formulate a rational, interrelated system of sensible and supersensible reality, which in its reasoned ordering is quite unlike any other occult or mystic teaching. Moreover, because of this basic element in it of rational thinking, his Spiritual Science can be understood by thinkers who have not themselves direct perception of spirit-realities, provided only that they free themselves from the prejudice against considering phenomena, which ordinary logical thinking, based on sense-perception and the successional time-consciousness of the physical world, cannot directly apprehend.

The seeker who has arrived at higher knowledge, or who has accepted the facts of higher knowledge as set before us by Steiner as the basis of his own thinking, finds himself in a completely new relation to the world, to his fellow human beings and to himself. No longer does man appear to him as a being experiencing a strange and inexplicable faculty of consciousness in complete loneliness from all other beings, on a tiny planet set in the midst of a vast universe, in which an endless number of material bodies move hither and thither through measureless empty spaces. The universe is now a world of countless spirit-beings, related to one another and functioning with each other in an ordered manner, and having a direct concern with the life of mankind on earth. Even spatially, he sees that he has lost his sense of loneliness, and that he is related to the whole universe. He has discovered that he is living in three worlds, the astral, the etheric and physical, the two former inter-penetrating the latter. Although the range of his physical experience is so limited that it seems quite unimportant in relation to the vast distances which surround him, yet he knows that, beyond the physical, extends the sphere of etheric influence which pours its life-giving forces and powers into his physical being; and beyond that again, the great sphere of the astral world, from which the subtler forces of consciousness and of moral and spiritual reality pour into his soul. The ancient world-concept of a concentric, geocentric universe seems utterly foolish to a man who views everything spatially and materially; but to men more conscious of their inner life than of their outer material surroundings, it was a concept that spoke of a true and deep experience. Without asserting the ultimate or sole importance of man and the earth, this present universe—as, by divine will, it now exists in time and space in relation to the evolution of man—is spiritually a geocentric, anthropocentric universe, in which man in his life on earth is surrounded, influenced and upheld by the great cosmic forces that pour into him. The knowledge of the higher worlds brings to earthly life a deep meaning and an ultimate importance. Man is revealed as the Psalmist with inner vision saw him, when he said that God had made him only a little lower than the angels, that thereby he might attain to the perfection of his being.

CHAPTER X

THE ORIGIN AND DESTINY OF MAN

ONE of the most important elements in Rudolf Steiner's Spiritual Science is his account of the origin and destiny of man. We have already seen that "higher" knowledge reveals that man is a spirit-being and that he cannot be explained in terms of a material origin. But Steiner goes much further than that. He gives, with most detailed exposition and analysis, a full account of man's spirit-origin and of his evolution through every stage to his present condition. Moreover, he claims that this account is not surmise or hypothesis, but is derived from factual observation of the historical phenomena, as they are preserved in what is called "The Akashic Record", i.e. the "Imperishable Record".

He writes of this "Akashic Record" in his book *An Outline of Occult Science*:

> The facts concerning the primeval past have not passed beyond the reach of occult research. If a being comes into corporeal existence, his material part perishes after physical death. But the spirit-forces, which, from out of their own depth, gave existence to the body, do not "disappear" in this way. They leave their traces, their exact images, behind them, impressed upon the spiritual groundwork of the world. Anyone who is able to raise his perceptive faculty through the visible to the invisible world, attains at length a level, on which he may see before him what may be compared to a vast spiritual panorama, in which are recorded all the past events of the world's history. These imperishable traces of everything immaterial are called in occult science the "Akashic Records".[1]

[1] An outline of *Occult Science*, p. 108.

In another passage he writes:

> Here [i.e. in quoting from the "Akashic Record"], it becomes an easy matter for the uninitiated (more especially if he is devoid as yet of any personal experience of spiritual worlds) to assume that his informant is enlarging on his own imagination. But those who have acquired the faculty of "seeing" in the spiritual worlds will be able to recognise the eternal pattern underlying those ephemeral events. Nor do they confront them in the capacity of "dead witnesses"; rather they are full of life—for it may be said that, to a certain extent, the past is re-enacted in the seer's presence.[1]

Now all this, as Steiner admits in the above passage, will appear, at first reading, quite incredible, and many will be inclined to dismiss it from their mind as valid evidence, particularly as, at the level of ordinary consciousness, it does not admit of first-hand verification. There are however other considerations to be borne in mind. In the first place, while Rudolf Steiner recognises this natural incredulity, he repeatedly makes the categorical statement that the Akashic Record is an objective reality, and he derives from it a rational and coherent account of the origin of the physical universe and of man. It would not only be difficult to invent this, but his whole life and character make it incredible that he should have deliberately invented it. Moreover, as he tells us, the main facts of this account have been given by others who have developed the faculty of spiritual vision, as a matter of direct observation of the same supersensible facts.[2] None, however, have interpreted their vision in such rationally-ordered detail, nor related it to the discoveries and conclusions of modern science, as Steiner did.

[1] *Atlantis and Lemuria*, p. 9.

[2] e.g. Mme Blavatsky and the earlier Rosicrucian mystics. These latter, however, expressed these truths in esoteric symbolic language.

The following short quotations are from the writings of two English seers. The first is from the seventeenth century poet, Thomas Traherne. "When the Bible was read my spirit was present in other ages. I saw the light and splendour of them, the Land of Canaan, the Israelities entering into it, the (*continued opposite*)

While, however, it is impossible for the ordinary reader, at the level of physical consciousness, to verify the fact of the Akashic Record, or clearly to visualise how it can be recorded and interpreted, there is a direct clue to the understanding of it, in what we have already seen to be one of the first experiences of the development of the faculty of supersensible perception. We saw that in "Imagination", the first level of higher knowledge, there is discovered the tableau of the whole past life of the seeker, as a living inter-related unity, in which past events are available to re-experience. Although the physical events happened in successional-time, and although as *physical* events, they and their material setting no longer exist, yet the inner experience of the individuals who took part in them belongs to a higher level of continuous Time-experience, in which the whole is preserved as experience and as an objective reality. Now this is true of the life of every individual, and although at first, it is only the tableau of his own life that appears to the seeker, it obviously must, as such, contain endless relationships with other people. As he progresses in spiritual knowledge in the astral world, which is the world of personal relationships, the seeker is able to enter into the experience of others besides himself.

It is clear, therefore, that the whole pattern of inter-related human experience must constitute a spiritual entity, which would be what Steiner describes as "a vast spiritual panorama of world-history". Moreover, higher knowledge reveals that, inter-related with human experience and behind the manifested life of material objects, is the activity of spirit-beings,

ancient glory of the Amorites, their peace and riches, their cities, houses, vines, and fig-trees, the long prosperity of their Kings. This shewed me that all ages were for most glorious ends acecssible to my understanding. For without changing place in myself I could behold and enjoy all those. Anything, when it was proposed, though it was a thousand ages ago, being always before me."—*Centuries of Meditations.*

The second quotation is from A. E. (G. W. Russell) in the early years of this century. "I was able at times to evoke deliberately, out of the memory of Nature, pictures of persons or things long past in time, but of which I desired knowledge. . . . The fact that Earth holds such memories is itself important, for once we discover the imperishable tablet, we are led to speculate whether in the future a training in seership might not lead to a revolution in human knowledge."—*The Candle of Vision.*

at varying levels of spirit-development, who do not incarnate in physical bodies. The pattern of all this spirit-activity is interwoven into the tableau, not only of human history, but of the whole history of the evolution of the universe in Time.

It is only, however, at the highest stage of spiritual perception, that the whole panorama of the Akashic Record becomes clear to the seeker and that he is able to decipher in it the pattern of primeval evolution. Even then, he has the difficult task of expressing, in logical, rational forms of thought, what he has deciphered. For that he needs the faculty of sense-independent thinking, of which we spoke in the last chapter. Of this Steiner writes:

> It cannot be sufficiently emphasised that an obligation is laid upon the explorer of supersensible regions, before he determines to approach the invisible worlds with his own power of perception, to acquire first of all the aforementioned logical faculty.[1]

Moreover, Steiner declares that in this rational interpretation of the Akashic Record there is the possibility of error.

> It may even happen [he writes], that an investigator who possesses the power of vision in supersensible spheres, may make mistakes in a logical presentment of them, and may be corrected by another who has no supersensible perception, but has, none the less, a capacity for sound thinking.[2]

While, therefore, the thinker, at the ordinary level of physical consciousness, is not able directly to apprehend the Akashic Record, nor the exact manner in which it is deciphered, yet the manifestation, in the early stages of spiritual investigation, of the reality of "continuous-Time-consciousness" would almost imply the existence of such a record of the past. Moreover, Steiner's rational exposition of his reading of the Akashic Record offers itself to the judgment of ordinary logical think-

[1] *An Outline of Occult Science*, p. 110.

[2] *An Outline of Occult Science*, p. 109.

ing, and of the ascertained scientific facts of the physical world of sense-experience.

Steiner set out his account of the evolution of the world and man at great length, in several books. It merits the most careful study and is open to fuller development and application to modern scientific thinking than has yet been given to it. A mere superficial reading of it from the point of view of ordinary physical experience will probably only confuse the mind of the reader. It can only be followed and understood in the light of the conditions of spirit-existence which Steiner reveals. All that it is possible to give here is a summary of the main features of this cosmic process and an indication of the principles of evolution involved in it.

The principle of the evolution of the Earth itself is that it is the expression of the creative activity of spirit-beings, in a succession of physical planetary conditions. Each of these conditions develops up to a certain point, after which the physical element is gradually dissolved again into its spiritual origins. While, however, the physical element is coming to an end, the spiritual form of a higher development is being evolved in it by the working of spirit-beings upon it, and, after the dissolution of the physical element, this passes into a spirit-existence, in which it is matured and given further possibilities of evolutionary development. It is then recreated as the germ of a new planetary condition. In the earlier part of this new planetary condition, the former stages of evolution are repeated, though much more rapidly than at the stage at which they were first evolved. Then a further evolutionary physical stage is reached by the action of spiritual beings, working on the new possibilities acquired out of the last planetary condition and developed in the intervening spiritual period of "rest".

This process is directly observed, in tracing back through the Akashic Record the cosmic history of our Earth-planet. Our Earth is the fourth of these planetary conditions, the first of which was an almost immaterial condition of warmth, to which was subsequently added an aeriform, and then a fluid condition, passing on to the present state of solid matter.

In this evolution of the Earth the being of man also evolved, not out of the substance of the evolving Earth, but, like it, out of the spiritual world, by the activity of spirit-beings. We have already seen, in our consideration of higher knowledge, that physical man, as he exists today, consists of four parts, the physical body, the etheric body, and the astral body, together with the ego, the spirit-core of the whole being. In the first three planetary conditions the three "bodies", through which the ego functions in the physical world, were successively evolved, and it was not until the present Earth conditions that the ego, the real spirit-essence of human individuality, could descend into these bodies and enter into a physical existence.

Here we touch another point of human evolution. In the first three periods of evolution "man" is not as yet present in his real individual being, but other spirit beings express themselves in and through the evolving physical, etheric and astral bodies, and in this way bring about their gradual development. In doing this the spirit-beings at the same time forward their own evolution. Until the point, in the present Earth-stage of evolution, at which the human ego descended into its evolved and inter-related "bodies", the being of man was, as it were, carried by higher beings. With the descent of the ego, "man" is created.

At this point a new stage in human evolution begins. Man, in his ego, is a spirit-being of the same nature as the beings through whose activity his three "bodies" have evolved. Now, more and more, he must work out on Earth his own evolution. Through these three bodies he begins to experience, and will gradually learn to understand and control, his physical environment, and, in so doing, he will not only acquire his own individual content of experience, *but he will develop in himself an ever-evolving soul-life.* This is, as it were an extension of his ego, as the result of the latter becoming successively conscious of the working of the three bodies of its human organism in relation to its physical environment.

This gradual evolution in mankind of a conscious soul-life is the clue to the interpretation of human history, but to understand its working we must glance again for a moment at the evolution of man in the present Earth planet. This, the fourth stage of cosmic evolution, consists of seven periods, of which we are now in the fifth. The first two, which covered vast ages of time, were a recapitulation of the earlier planetary evolution of man, and it was not until the middle of the third period that we have the beginning of the descent of the human ego into its evolved bodies. Geographically, the evolution of mankind during this Age took place on the continent of Lemuria, which extended over what is now the Indian Ocean, Southern Asia and part of Africa. In his inner life man was still consciously under the guidance of spirit-beings, among whom were some inimical to the divine plan of human evolution. These are the spirits whom Steiner designates as the Luciferic spirits. He speaks of them collectively as "Lucifer." Under their influence man sought a measure of independence from the guidance of higher spirit-beings and, as a result, man's ego became too deeply interfused with his material environment. This is described in the Bible in the story of the "Fall". In this period ego-evolution developed little further than the fashioning of the form of the physical body to be a more adequate instrument for the ego.

This period, known as the Lemurian Age, came to an end in a volcanic cataclysm, and the surviving most highly-developed members of the human race moved north-westwards, to the continent of Atlantis, which extended over the area of the present Atlantic Ocean and its American and European shores. In the Atlantean Age man's inner life developed, by the ego beginning to express itself in the etheric body. Mankind did not yet live by reason, but by the development of an almost continuous memory, and by an intuitive understanding of his environment, which gave him power to control and use the forces of Nature. In this age, too, the power of speech developed, and mankind began to be differentiated into races, at different cultural and moral levels.

Atlantean man still had some vision of the spirit-world, and, in varying degrees, he was under the influence of spirit-beings, both beneficent and corrupting. He especially fell under the influence of certain spirits, who drew him still more deeply into the physical world and clouded his spiritual understanding.

These were spirits who belonged entirely to the material world, in which Lucifer had already involved mankind. Steiner calls them "Ahrimanic", or, collectively, "Ahriman". Lucifer and Ahriman are the two opponents of man's spiritual evolution. Lucifer tempts man into spiritual independence of higher beings. Ahriman seeks to establish a material earthly kingdom, independent of the spiritual, and he seeks to draw man down into it, and to detach him from his spiritual destiny. These are the two destructive forces in human nature—self-sufficiency and materialism.[1]

There were, however, in Atlantis, certain human beings who kept themselves from excessive harmful influence, and, by the fact that their etheric body was not wholly identified with the physical, were able to develop their direct knowledge of the spiritual world. These grouped themselves at Oracles or Mystery-centres, and became the spiritual and cultural leaders of Atlantean mankind.

This civilisation also was overwhelmed, this time in a violent catastrophe of storm and flood, concerning which the Akashic Record supports the Biblical account, in shewing it to have been the result of the widespread moral depravity of man, in which even some of the Mystery-centres were involved.

Most of the survivors of this disaster migrated eastwards to Africa, Europe and Asia, and with them began the present, Fifth or post-Atlantean Age, in which the history of the human race, as we know it, lies. The physical body of man was no longer in the mobile, malleable form which man had possessed right into the Atlantean Age, but it had hardened into a fixed, solid form, in which it was no longer directly moulded by the

[1] In their original relation to human evolution Lucifer and Ahriman were not evil. Lucifer brought to man self-consciousness and Ahriman that awareness of the material world by which alone that self-consciousness could further develop. It is only by the one-sided, unbalanced expression of these spiritual forces in human evolution that they have become destructive.

soul, but was, for the most part, subject to earthly forces. Owing to the fact that no portion of the etheric body now remained free of the physical body, man had no longer any vision of his spiritual environment, and his great powers of memory grew less. At the same time the faculty of thought and reason was beginning to awaken in him. This was the instrument by means of which he was to experience and understand the physical world, and it was in doing this that he would develop the soul-evolution of which we have spoken.

The Initiates who survived the Atlantean Flood accompanied the migrations, and a group of the very highest, under a supreme leader, established themselves in Central Asia, where had gathered the most highly-developed Atlantean races. Inasmuch as man had no longer any direct knowledge of the spirit-world, and could only continue his evolution by penetrating more and more deeply into his physical environment by the awakening power of thought, it was vitally important to provide him with spiritual guidance. Under this supreme Initiate a few chosen leaders were initiated, who could present to the awakening human thought the whole picture of the divine, unseen background of existence, and who could train others to develop their own faculties of spirit-perception. Thus were carried into the post-Atlantean Age the great Mystery-centres, which for millennia were the source of human spiritual and cultural development.

The usual scientific account of man's historical evolution is based on the stages by which he conquered his physical environment, the Stone Age, the Bronze Age, the Iron Age—up to the modern ages of Steam, Electricity and Atomic Energy. But Spiritual Science divides human history in the post-Atlantean Age into successive epochs, each of which marks a stage *in the evolution of the human soul*, through the ever-developing consciousness in the ego, of the working of its astral, etheric and physical bodies.

The first of these epochs is called "The Ancient Indian Civilisation" and begins in the eighth millennium before Christ. The post-Atlantean peoples who dwelt in India at that time had no longer direct spiritual vision, but they were a people whose awakening powers of thought had not led them, as deeply as it had others, into the material world. They had an intense innate longing for the spiritual world and regarded the material world and their physical bodies as "Maya", or illusion, from which they longed to escape back to the spirit-world of their origin. Among such a people the teaching of the Great Initiates created "a civilisation completely saturated with supersensible wisdom. The contents of the books of wisdom of the Hindus, the Vedas, do not give the original form of this lofty wisdom, only a feeble echo of it."[1] In this civilisation the human ego only slowly and unwillingly developed its experience of the etheric-physical body, and under the guidance of the spiritual world. The experience did not yet play into or fashion the inner consciousness of the ego.

The second epoch is called "The Ancient Persian Civilisation". It arose in the fifth millennium B.C. in the highlands of the present Persia, among a people who still cherished a knowledge of the spirit-world, and retained from a past age certain supersensible powers of a lower, almost magical, kind, which gave them something of the old Atlantean control over the forces of Nature. They were an active and vigorous people, with an awareness of both worlds, but the danger was that they should regard their spirit faculties only as a means to a more intensive and effective material existence. This danger was met by the teaching of the great Initiate of the Sun Oracle in Persia, Zarathustra.[2] He taught that the physical world is not mere lifeless matter for man's use or enjoyment, but that behind it is a world of spirit. He revealed too the nature of the great Sun Spirit, the God of Light with his angelic ministers, and showed that he was in constant conflict in the souls of men against Ahriman, the enemy of man's spiritual evolution, and his hosts of darkness. In this conflict man was called upon to take his part. He also revealed a great

[1] *An Outline of Occult Science*, p. 248.

[2] The written record of the teaching of Zarathustra—as of the Indian sacred writings—is of much later date. The explanation of this is given in a later chapter, see p. 157.

truth—that is repeated, in one form or another, through all subsequent religions—namely, that the Sun-Spirit, Ahura Mazdao, was moving to man's rescue, and that one day, when a suitable human body could be evolved, he would descend into it and defeat Ahriman. This was the era of the spiritually-guided development of the astral body in relation to the ego.

At the beginning of the third millennium B.C., the third epoch of post-Atlantean evolution came into being, in the Assyrian-Babylonian and Egyptian Civilisations. In the first two epochs, the Ancient Indian and Ancient Persian Civilisations, the ego had adapted itself to the working of the etheric-physical and astral bodies. In both civilisations there had still remained an actual connection with the spirit-world, and man's earthly experience was interpreted and guided by the spiritual wisdom of the Mystery-centres. Man's own experience of the earth had not yet begun to affect the inner consciousness of his ego.

But in the third epoch man arrived at clearer and more sustained personal consciousness of his contact with the physical world, through the development of the ego's experience of the working of the astral body, the vehicle of conscious experience. This marked another advance in the spiritual evolution of mankind, for with the development of his astral body, man began to have an inner consciousness, a conscious soul-life. As a result of his enriched life of feeling and sense-experience there developed in man the "sentient-soul", and human life became largely governed by emotion and desire.

Although—except in the Mysteries—man had lost all direct connection with the spirit-world, he still believed in a spirit-origin and a spirit-future, and he regarded the physical world—and especially the heavenly bodies—as a manifestation of spirit-activity. He strove constantly to understand the spiritual laws underlying physical phenomena, and in this way he advanced his understanding of them. In regard to his own spirit-being, man felt that on earth he could no longer live as spirit, but that, by his earthly life, he could win the possibility of a return after death to a spirit-existence.

The Egyptian religion of Isis expressed this sense of the immediate loss of spirit-experience and the hope of its recovery. This was an age of highly cultural civilisations, as archæological exploration has revealed.

The fourth epoch of the post-Atlantean Age coincides with the Græco-Roman Civilisation, beginning about the eighth century B.C. It arose amongst vigorous peoples, who had not shared in the developed civilisations of Asia, but who had natural gifts of clairvoyance, and traditions of lesser Atlantean Mysteries which sought to find the spiritual behind natural phenomena. In this epoch the ego became conscious of the faculties of man's own being by means of which he is abie to enter into experience of the physical world—in other words, it became inwardly conscious of the working of the etheric body. Man had now no knowledge of the spiritual world, except through myth and legend or by initiation into the Mysteries, but he became increasingly conscious of his own powers of intellect, creative ability, artistic imagination, and moral judgment. All this knowledge of the working of man's etheric body had been conveyed to man in the past by spirit-beings or through the teaching of the Mystery-schools, but it now seemed to him to arise out of his own being. This new stage in human soul-experience Steiner describes as the evolution of the Intellectual-soul, or the Mind-soul. It was no wonder that man, at the first-flowering of this consciousness in Greece, tried to express the spiritual in the perfection of human sense-existence, and fashioned the gods in the likeness of himself. Man, however, gradually lost all sense of his spirit-origin, and, in his glorification of human sense-existence, came to regard the life after death with fear and repugnance, as a shadowy—and unreal existence.

With the rise of the Roman civilisation there was an ever-stronger tendency towards the physical experience of the sense-perceived world, and lack of knowledge of the spirit-world turned to scepticism. This tendency was increased by Rome's acceptance of the corrupt materialism of the conquered East. Indeed so entirely was life concentrated upon the physical world, that even those who still had faith in a future existence, began to doubt whether man could ever find his way to it. Nor were their fears unfounded. The victory of Ahriman, the prince of this world, over the divine purpose of human destiny, seemed complete. The New Testament describes the Roman world as "without God and without hope", "those who through fear of death, were all their lifetime subject to bondage". The *ascent* of man in his knowledge and enjoyment of the physical world, had been accompanied by a disastrous *descent* into a complete separation from his spiritual origin and environment, and an alienation from his spiritual destiny.

It was at this moment in the evolution of mankind that Christ came into the world—the fulfilment of the prophetic vision of the Ancient Mysteries and the Jewish prophets, and of the wistful longing of mankind. The Christ-event is in Steiner's world-picture the pivotal point in the evolution of mankind, right through from its earliest beginnings to its far-distant fulfilment. We shall consider it in more detail in a later chapter, but we can see its vital significance in this account of the soul-evolution of humanity. Into this sense-ridden, sceptical world Christ brought the message and power of the spirit-world itself, "the kingdom of heaven", with a new certainty of life after death, and an assurance that behind the physical world was not only the creative act, but the ceaseless care and activity of the seemingly-lost spirit-world. By his divine act on Golgotha he sowed a seed of life, that ensured the spiritual future of humanity against the twin corrupting powers of self-sufficiency and materialism. By this deed he awakened in men's hearts a response of love and devotion that overcame the pride and decadence of Rome, and nursed the new civilisation of Europe through the dark days of its infancy. The flower of that seed is barely open yet; its full fruit has yet to ripen.

But with all its darkness and vicissitudes, this epoch is clearly the age of the Intellectual Soul. From the miracle of the flowering of Athens, through Plato, Aristotle, Plotinus, right up to Thomas Aquinas at its close, the great thinkers of mankind were absorbed in the wonder of man's own being, in its working in the world of sense-experience, and in its relation to the spirit-world.

The fifth epoch of post-Atlantean civilisation, the epoch we live in, is the third stage of the soul-evolution of the human ego. It began in the fifteenth century, in the European civilisation which had arisen when the Germanic peoples overwhelmed and gradually absorbed the Græco-Roman civilisation. These Germanic races were descendants of Atlantean peoples, who had remained quite unaffected by the post-Atlantean civilisations. They retained a complete belief in the spirit-world, and, in many cases, they still possessed the ancient clairvoyance. There were varied Mysteries in existence among them. Some of them were directed, like the Mysteries of the East, to the riddle of man's own spiritual being, and in the myths—in which the Mysteries in every age spoke to the ordinary man—there are obvious parallels to the Asian and Greek Mysteries.

But these races were vigorous and strongly individualistic, and, probably through the compulsion of rigorous climatic conditions, were compelled to direct their attention and energy to the physical world, which they sought to master to their use. There were among them other Mysteries, that sought the spiritual in and behind natural phenomena, and to these Mysteries they were deeply attached, seeking through them further power over the physical world.

There were thus in the Germanic peoples two separate streams; one from the Mysteries of the human spirit, which, even when there was no clairvoyance, held strongly their feelings and emotion, particularly in regard to a life after death; and the other from the Mysteries of Nature, in the attachment of their powers of thought and will to the unveiling and mastery of the secrets of the Earth. Christianity made a strong appeal to their feelings and devotion, but even there the cleavage remained, as can be seen in the intellectual vigour of the Arian heresy and the continual conflict of Emperor and Pope, and in the opposition of the Church to the alchemists and, later, to the new age of Reason.

This European civilisation—as is always the case in evolution, whether collective or individual—recapitulated the past. The sixth to the tenth centuries saw the development in it of the Sentient Soul, particularly in the south of Europe, where the victors took eager possession of the highly-developed, though decadent, civilisation of Rome. The next four centuries were the age of the Intellectual Soul, when Scholasticism arose, through the challenge of Arabian philosophy to the formal dogmatism of the Church. In Thomas Aquinas, European civilisation raised the power of pure thought to a height comparable with that of Aristotle and Plotinus, and prepared the way for the new stage in evolution, the fifth post-Atlantean epoch, the epoch of modern civilisation.

This began in the fifteenth century, when, in the Renaissance, the returning flood of Greek learning quickened man's ever-deepening interest in unveiling the secrets of the physical world, by the newly-discovered method of inductive thought based on nothing but direct sense-experience. In this pursuit of the understanding and mastery of the physical world, the spirit-world had no part. While for faith, religious devotion, and the hope of a future life the Christian message still held sway, in the sphere of scientific investigation it had no place. Human thought was no longer a spiritual-physical mystery. It was merely a faculty arising in and out of the physical organism of man, to enable him to understand and conquer the world he lived in. This is the epoch of the Consciousness-Soul, or the object-conscious soul, the age of scientific mastery of the material world. It is also the age of ego-consciousness. In perceiving more clearly the objective world, man becomes conscious of himself as subject. This ego-consciousness is entirely related to man's experience of his environment through his physical body—its physical relation to himself as a physical being. He becomes conscious of himself, both as the subject standing over against the manifold objectivity of the physical world, and also as the source of the marvellous process of scientific, sense-derived knowledge.

More recently, man has become aware of himself in another light, as an object of his own scientific investigation in his inner being. But where the age of the Intellectual Soul saw intimations of spirit, all is explained in terms of sense-experience and physical organs.

This is the dualism of Reason and Faith of which we spoke in the Introduction, and before which man stands, either bewildered or unthinking. For scientific knowledge points to no human destiny but death, to no world destiny but material disintegration. Faith points to the future, but makes no valid claim to interpret the present, except as a preparation for that future. Such a dualism will not stand for ever. Political Communism has already resolved it, by the rejection of Faith. It seems like another victory for the enemy of the spiritual destiny of mankind.

Yet it is just at this point that Rudolf Steiner reveals the next immediate step towards that destiny. There is no call for a retreat. The step lies before us. The path of scientific knowledge, that has brought man to this seeming impasse, is the true path of man's spiritual destiny. What man now needs to do is to develop the scientific instrument of human thought to a higher level, along the line of its own pure activity, and reclothe it with some of the spiritual understanding which former ages possessed. Then it will become an instrument of scientific investigation that will pass the imposed bounds of sense-experience, and arrive at a clear understanding of the spirit-background of the physical world and of human history. Ego-consciousness will become consciousness of itself as a spirit-being, and the Consciousness Soul will become the Spirit-self.

If that step is taken, it will be the beginning of man's re-ascent to a spirit-awareness, lit by clear thought and moral freedom. Beyond it there still lies the further destiny of man's earthly evolution, when his Spirit-self, that in its self-discovery will have spiritualised the astral organ of its experience, shall, in future times, spiritualise also its etheric and physical bodies.

CHAPTER XI

THE EVOLUTION OF THE INDIVIDUAL—THE PROCESS OF REINCARNATION

We have considered the evolution of the Earth and of mankind as they are revealed in Spiritual Science, but we have not yet considered the place of the individual human being in this vast process. Sc far, he only appears as a transient element in the evolution of the human race, appearing for a very short space of time at some particular stage in it. The fundamental eternal importance of the individual has always been a central idea in Western civilisation, based as it has been upon Christian teaching and European individualism, and, as we have seen, nothing works more havoc in the stability of modern consciousness, than the difficulty of reconciling this instinct with modern scientific discovery and political totalitarianism.

Even in Christianity itself it is not easy to reconcile its insistence on the eternal value of the individual and the primary importance for each human being of the salvation which is in Christ, with the facts of life and history. What about the individuals who, by time or place, by cultural or moral environment, have been completely isolated from the knowledge of Christianity? What about those who by mental deficiency or early death have never reached an age of understanding? Christian theology has attempted to answer these queries in different ways, either by completely denying to such individuals any hope of spiritual evolution, or by limiting the level to which they can ever attain. But the more optimistic wishful thinking of today is inclined to leave it all to the mercy of God, and to believe that these individuals will find after death, in the spiritual world, the opportunity for salvation and spiritual perfection which their earthly conditions denied them. The difficulty in accepting such an explanation is twofold; for if human perfection can be attained in the spirit-world, it is difficult to see any necessity for a physical existence; and still less, for the fact, central to the Christian faith, of the incarnation of Christ in human form.

The attempt to explain human existence in terms of a single earth-life becomes still more difficult when we consider the account of world-evolution that Spiritual Science sets before us. For there we see the whole history of mankind as the continuous process of the evolution of human consciousness under the conditions of physical life on this Earth, a process the goal of which still lies in the future. What relation to such a process can individual human beings have, in one short life at one point in it?

To this question Spiritual Science gives a clear and comprehensive answer, which fits the individual completely into this evolutionary process. The evolution of the individual is based upon the same principle that we have seen in the evolution of the human race and of the Earth itself; namely, a descent from a spirit-condition into a physical condition, which develops up to a certain point, after which the physical condition is dissolved, while the spirit-fruit of it returns to a spirit-condition. In this it receives the possibilities and powers for a further evolutionary development, after which it returns once more to a new earthly existence.

The evolution of man *as an individual being* began at that point in race-evolution at which the human ego, the individual human spirit-entity, began to descend into the three "bodies" of its physical existence, the astral, etheric and physical, which had been developed by the creative work of spirit-beings in previous planetary conditions. This, as we have seen, took place in the middle of the Lemurian Age.

This principle of individual evolution is that of reincarnation, which, as we have seen, is revealed as a historical fact to one who develops his organs of supersensible preception to the level of higher knowledge. Now, although reincarnation has always been accepted as true by the greater part of the human race, it has never been a concept in Western civilisation, nor has it been taught by the Christian faith, and it presents many difficulties to generally-accepted scientific ideas and to traditional Christian thinking. We shall try to meet these difficulties at a later stage, when we have first considered the nature and working of the process of reincarnation as set out in Spiritual Science.

Our examination of this recurring cycle of earthly and spiritual lives could begin at any point, and we will take as our point of departure the moment of earthly death. The advantage of this is that this is the point at which human wonder and speculation begins, and also that, leading up to it, is that part of our existence of which we are fully conscious.

Already, in our study of the path to higher knowledge, we have become cognisant of higher worlds, higher levels of consciousness and being, which interpenetrate our earthly existence and stretch far beyond its bounds. It is into these worlds that we pass in death, but, whereas in higher knowledge we advance by temporarily discarding the conditions of lower consciousness, in death the wearing out of our physical organism releases us perforce to a progressive experience of these spiritual worlds, which we cannot evade. In books and in many lectures Steiner set out in great detail the stages of this spiritual pilgrimage of man, not only describing them, but revealing them as the ordered working of the great principles of metamorphosis between matter and spirit, and between time and eternity, and of moral law working immutably in the passage from one stage to another. All this he relates as the result of his own direct supersensible perception. It would be quite impossible in this general introduction to his teaching, to set out these facts or follow the working of these processes in detail. The reader will find them set out in Dr. Wachsmuth's closely-reasoned presentation and application of Steiner's teaching on this subject.[1] All we can do is to present the stages of this spiritual ascent and descent of the human

[1] *Reincarnation*, by Dr. Günther Wachsmuth. (Rudolf Steiner Publishing Co., London.)

spirit in such a way, that they may make plain the ordered working of reincarnation in the evolution of the individual.

The first and immediate result of the falling away of the physical body in death is that the individual ego, now clothed only in the astral and etheric bodies, becomes aware of the etheric time-tableau of the whole earth-life, of which we have already spoken in our consideration of "higher knowledge". This etheric tableau of life's inter-related events fades away in a few days, as the etheric body, having no longer its function of fashioning and sustaining the physical body, also falls away from the individual and is reabsorbed into the general substance of the etheric world. Already, however, the etheric life-tableau has imprinted itself indelibly on the astral body, in which now the ego wholly dwells. In doing this, the tableau has undergone a metamorphosis. No longer is it merely an inter-related time-unity of earthly events, but in the astral world of desire and emotion it has been transmuted into a qualitative reality of personal relationships, the moral implication of which is apparent to the human ego—a judgment in which it feels the concurrence of the spiritual world.

Here we have the second metamorphosis of consciousness, which we encountered, in the chapter on the search for Higher Knowledge, as the level of "Inspiration".[1] The sequence of events which formed the earth-life is still present as a time-unity, but their significance is now altered. On earth a man's life appeared as a series of events which happened to himself as an individual, as one who, in spite of all his relationships with others, retained his own *separate identity*. But now he perceives that really this was not so. He has now reached the astral world, which was revealed, at the level of "Inspiration", as consisting only of personal relationships, and there he sees that similar conditions existed, unperceived, in his earth-life. Even there his being was not, as he thought, entirely contained within his own skin, but it partook of the relationships which he experienced with others; so that these relationships were inwrought into his being. Even the sufferings that he brought on others he now feels within himself as his own.

[1] See p. 88.

"With what measure ye mete it shall be measured to you again." Earth-life no longer appears to consist merely of events linked together in time by natural law and logical sequence. It appears to be much more fundamentally a vast pattern of human relationships, into which the life of every man and woman is interwoven to a far wider extent than he ever imagined. Our earthly relationships are seen to be a part of our very being. Indeed a vital moral consequence of the earth-life is revealed, in the discovery that the possibility of entering into true relationship with other beings, which is the whole life of the spirit-world, is dependent upon whether in our earth-life we have manifested unselfishness or egoism.

So overwhelming is this new understanding of man's earthly existence, that the ego after death is not concerned, in the astral world, with tracing the time-sequence of his earthly life, but is absorbed in unravelling this pattern of moral relationships in which his being is implicated. He begins to re-experience his past earthly life from its end back to its beginning.

This reversal of experience does not mean that individual deeds are experienced "backwards", but that the order of events is reversed. The significance of this is that the events are not re-experienced in their time-sequence of physical cause and effect, but in their moral incidence and necessity, the moral significance of any re-experienced deed or word or relationship, being heightened by the immediate pre-experience of its consequence, in what had been on earth a subsequent event. It is an unravelling of a pattern of moral consequence, not a mere re-experience of events.

In such a retrospect the essential validity of moral values becomes self-evident. Indeed, the main purpose of this "retrospect" is to integrate man's earthly experience into his eternal spirit-being, and for this the first essential is the purification of it from those desires and habits that can only be satisfied by material means. For such earthly defects would make impossible the soul's further experience of the spirit-world.

The purging from its earthly defects, however, is not the

only process to which this re-experience of the earthly life is subject. We have already spoken of the moral judgment which the soul passes upon its earthly past. In the spiritual world such judgment is not merely a matter of evaluation or remorse. The desire to alter the pattern of behaviour or to right a wrong that awakens in the human being, becomes a creative force which implants in him the impulses towards such conditions and personal relationships in his next-earth-life, as shall make these desired amends possible. Here we have the beginning of Karma. We also here discover the objective spiritual value of judgment.

This period of purification can be a difficult and painful experience, as all religions have testified. In Eastern occultism this region of soul-experience is called "Kamaloca"; in Christian thought "Purgatory" or "Judgment". In Spiritual Science it is usually spoken of as the astral world or the soul-world. The relation of the deed of Christ to this experience is dealt with in a subsequent chapter.

At the end of this period the soul-spiritual being prepares to enter a new level of spirit-consciousness and it turns from the contemplation of its own earthly life-experience that has occupied it in the soul-world, to the experience of the great cosmic spirit-world. It leaves behind it its astral body of subjective soul-experience, and enters, as pure spirit, into the spirit-world. The quality of the soul's experience in this pure spirit-existence, and the extent to which it is able to carry down into another earth-life the fruits of its experience, vary according to the level of spiritual evolution to which it has attained.

In this experience of the passage from the astral to the spirit-world we recognise the third metamorphosis of consciousness to the level of "Intuition", on the path to Higher Knowledge. In both the etheric-physical and astral worlds the earthly life was seen to have a far higher significance than had been apparent to physical consciousness, and in certain respects, the experience of the soul was still related to the earthly conditions of space and time. But in the life of pure spirit, space and time no longer exist as a conditioning environment, but only as *media* of experience and self-expression, which a spirit-being can use freely and independently. In the spirit-world the personal relationships experienced on earth in time and space are metamorphosed into the spirit's actual being, and time and space—in their earthly significance—pass away. The only "environment" of pure spirit-existence is the eternal wisdom and will of God, with which all higher spirit-beings are freely and fully in harmony. It is in this vast pattern of related *being*, into which the deeds and relationships of earthly life are finally metamorphosed, that there is to be found that eternal, indestructible picture of all that has ever happened, which is called the Akashic Record.

Rudolf Steiner declares that it is impossible to describe adequately, in the language of physical consciousness, the life of these regions of pure spirit, but for the human ego it is a mounting experience of the creative activity of the hierarchic beings, and a revelation of the interworking, in the physical universe, of spirit and matter, which is an experience of the purest bliss. In relation to the Time-frame of human evolution, the passage through the world of pure spirit occupies a vastly longer period than that spent in the astral world.

Now, in regard to this ascent to higher worlds Steiner makes a revelation of great interest and importance, which it is impossible to deal with adequately in an introductory book of this sort. Nevertheless some reference must be made to it, as it keeps recurring from time to time in the descriptions which he gives of the spiritual worlds. This revelation may be called that of "Spiritual Astronomy". He reveals that man's life, physical and spiritual, is intimately related to the whole universe of stars, sun and planets. We have already pointed out that all material objects are a manifestation of spirit activity. In the same way the heavenly bodies are not mere meaningless masses moving through space, but they are the self-manifestation of spiritual beings, who radiate spiritual and moral forces within their spheres. These "spheres" are not to be identified with the luminous bodies we see in the heavens. So far as it can be spoken of spatially, the spiritual "sphere" of the planet is the field of operation of its forces, which is the whole sphere which is enclosed in the orbit which the visible planet describes in the heavens. The spiritual forces of these spheres inter-penetrate and are inter-related in manifold ways, but at certain points the influence of one sphere will predominate.

These astral forces work, unperceived, upon man during his life on earth, but the passage of the soul between death and rebirth is a conscious passage through the heavenly spheres. This must not be conceived as though it were the movement of a physical object towards a distant luminous body, in the way in which we speak of "a journey to Mars". Rather it is, as we saw in higher knowledge, the expansion of human consciousness from one sphere of spiritual experience to another. In the Moon-sphere man's soul-spiritual being is still earth-directed to his past life; but in the inner-planetary spheres of Venus and Mercury, his consciousness begins to expand to awareness of the beings of the soul-world. This is the astral world. In the Sun-sphere he arrives at the understanding of his own true ego, and, finally, expanding through the outer planetary spheres to the universe of stars, he arrives at his relationship to the whole spiritual universe. This is the world of pure spirit.

Rudolf Steiner says of this cosmic journey of the soul:

> The life between death and a new birth is really a living through the world of stars; but this means, through the *spirit* of the world of stars, through living together with the divine spiritual beings of the star-world.

In regard to the statement that these heavenly spheres are spiritual in their true nature, it may be objected that the visible heavenly bodies are related to each other and to man in terms of space and time, under which physical astronomy studies them. This of course is unquestionable, but it fits entirely into the spirit-astronomy which we have described. Spiritual Science reveals that the whole universe is related to spiritual evolution, and the whole visible universe to the evolution of mankind in physical consciousness, *in a frame-*

work of time and space. In the great act of the creation of such a framework the whole universe of spirit-beings has united. For in the configuration of their visible manifestation in the heavens and in their inter-related movements, man first became aware of time and space, of which they still are the ultimate reference and framework. This majestic celestial framework, however, is not the full measure of the service to mankind of these great spirit-beings, and it does not preclude their bestowal of moral and spiritual influences, as higher knowledge reveals, and as man discovers in his life after death. Nor is it conceivable that their own spirit-life and activity are limited to this visible manifestation as the framework of time and space, which they have created and which they continually sustain. Even if, with the evolution of the human race beyond fixed temporal and spatial categories, that framework of time and space should eventually disappear—"the stars shall fall from heaven"—the eternal spiritual life of the universe of Spirit-Being would still continue.

This relationship of the cosmos to man was known in the ancient world, but, as physical consciousness evolved, it was more and more lost. Modern popular astrology deals with partially-understood fragments of this ancient star-wisdom, and generally applies them in a superstitious and materialistic manner, which is quite different from the recovery and rational interpretation of that wisdom which is given in Spiritual Science.

To return to the passage of the human spirit through the spirit-world, when it has reached the summit of its experience in the world of pure spirit, there awakens in it a desire to perfect further the evolution of its own being and of the earth, and to remedy the wrong relationships into which it has brought itself. It begins to experience a longing to return to the earth. Therewith begins the soul's descent, during the first part of which it beholds the fashioning, by the highest creator spirits, of the spirit-germ[1] of its own future physical body, in accordance with the laws of the metamorphosis of

[1] This spirit-germ is of cosmic derivation, and must not be conceived of in terms of the minuteness associated with the common use of the word 'germ'.

deed and character into etheric forces and physical form. Continuing its descent, the spirit reaches again the soul-region, where it reclothes itself with an astral body of soul-experience, in accordance with the evolved nature and needs of its being. At that point the vision of the world of pure spirit fades from its consciousness, though the impulses derived from it remain.

Descending further, the incarnating ego chooses the hereditary line and actual parents, who will provide the suitable physical germ of material substance for its earth-life. This is one of the great truths that Spiritual Science reveals, that parents provide only the seed-bed of physical substance, impregnated with their own characteristics of temperament, and that, in the act of conception, material substance is broken down to the germinal level of chaos, in which all physical form is dissolved. Into this the spirit-germ of the new physical body descends, expressing its own spirit-created form in this inherited physical substance![1]

The descent of the spirit-germ of the body into the physical embryo takes place while the ego is still in the astral world. Then the latter, with the help of higher spirit-beings, fashions, from the etheric cosmos, the etheric body. This body of creative thought-forces, expresses, in a general pattern of circumstance and events in the coming earth-life, the fruits of the ego's experience in the spirit-world, and the karmic necessities of its being and personal relationships which are the result of its past earth-life. The fashioning of the etheric body is the process of the metamorphosis of spirit-being into Time-conditions, and this etheric body will be the continually moulding force of the new earth-life.

Then the ego, with the astral and etheric bodies, descends to unite with the embryo in the mother's womb, and the whole remembrance of the previous spirit-experience passes away from the incarnating being. This "forgetting" is necessary if man is to evolve his spirit-being in his physical life in freedom.

Thus the new earth-life begins and, just as Spiritual Science

[1] cf. Maurice Nicoll in *Living Time*, p. 38. "The spermatic power is really in the 'idea' rather than in the seed, and flows as a current through to the seed, when the right conditions for nurture exist".

throws light upon the completely unknown life between death and a new birth, so it also throws the most remarkable light upon the whole of man's earth-life. Here there is much greater opportunity of testing the revelations of Spiritual Science, by applying to them the facts of scientific knowledge in all departments of human life.

The embryonic life of the child, as science has long taught, recapitulates not only its own existence, but that of the race. This is proved completely true by Spiritual Science and it can be shown how the embryo retraces the whole course of spiritual evolution, both of itself and of the race, as higher knowledge reveals it to have taken place. At first the life of the united spirit-germ and physical germ in the embryo is entirely maintained by the etheric and astral forces of the mother. Although the ego, with the astral and etheric bodies, unites with the embryo in a comparatively short time, yet they do not at once take any active part in its development. It is not until the seventh week that the etheric forces, and at the seventh month the astral, and only just before birth the ego, work upon the life of the embryo, and even then they only do it through the maternal sheaths.

When at birth the child is delivered from the maternal sheath which has nourished its body, and is placed in its external surroundings, there begins a life in which two sets of forces are face to face. The spirit-germ of the body is now clothed with physical substance drawn from the life of the parents, and carrying with it certain inherited temperamental qualities. Over against this is the pre-earthly ego with its astral and etheric bodies, and human life consists in the process whereby the ego takes possession of this "model" presented to it by heredity, and works into it that pattern of life which it has brought with it from the spirit-world. That work does not commence at once, for the ego does not really enter actively into the bodily life of the child until the third or fourth year, while the pre-earthly etheric and astral bodies remain, enclosed, as it were in an embryonic sheath in the child, and do not emerge to function independently until the seventh and fourteenth years respectively.

Every seven years the substance of the human body is replaced, and at the seventh year we no longer have in the child the physical body bequeathed by the parents, but one in which the ego has already begun to express physically the pre-earthly spirit-germ of the body. This is signified by the change of teeth at about the seventh year. Already the ego in the child is expressing some of the temperamental qualities which it brought with it from previous lives. It is clearly noticeable that, after the age of seven, a child begins to individualise itself far more out of its resemblance, even its physical resemblance, to its parents. At this age the child begins to enter into the conscious functioning of its own etheric body, which impresses its individual qualities into the inherited etheric life. At fourteen the astral body comes into conscious development and again the same process is repeated. At the age of twenty-one the ego itself awakes to self-consciousness, equipped with the three bodies, physical, etheric and astral, which are the earthly expression of its pre-earthly, karmically-fashioned being. Of course in all this process there are also present the inherited tendencies of the parents and also the social influences of the home and of the educators of the child, upon all of which the individual ego, with varying completeness, impresses the pattern of its own being. In his adult life the individual has now to function with these three developed bodies, and to fashion for himself his own life-experience, which he must transform into qualities, characteristics, and faculties which he can carry with him beyond death. At the end of his life his physical forces gradually fail, and then death completes the great cycle of existence which we have been considering.

The frequency of reincarnation is not a rigid matter and may depend upon special circumstances. Normally, the soul incarnates twice in each great period of soul-evolution, once as a man and once as a woman, as the soul of each individual is both male and female. This would normally mean an incarnation about once every thousand years. The power that lifts the race from one level of soul-development to another, is provided by those advanced spirits who are able to rise in their life between death and re-birth to the highest level of spirit-experience, and to bring back with them knowledge and power for new development.

We see Reincarnation then, as a great rhythm of being, through which man, as a spirit-being, passes continually from a spirit-existence to a physical one, and back again, in a gradual ascent of spiritual evolution. It is a quite wrong approach to the subject to speak about it as if it were merely a matter of repeated earth-lives. It is materialistic curiosity to speculate as to what position in the world one held in a former earth-life. What really matters, is to understand the nature of one's being in this life, to see the revelation in it of mistakes and failures, as well as of achievements, brought into it from the past, and to live it out with the sure knowledge that the fruit of it must be carried into a future existence, up to a final spiritual goal of being.

In the same way, in talking about "Karma", we must be very sure that we understand what it really is. This great law of consequence and metamorphosis, working out in moral, psychic, physical and circumstantial ways, is often interpreted merely as a sort of punishment or doom for past sins, or as some irrevocable fate; or, sometimes, it is made a justification for all sorts of actions, as though by Karma we were compelled to act in a certain way.

Karma arises out of the fact of man's essential being as an eternal spirit. Man is a being who lives, in the spirit-world, a life of endless relationships to other beings, and also to the divine ordering of the universe. His life on earth is the expression of that same eternal being in terms of successional time-experience. Nevertheless, it is still that same eternal being who is living under this physical time-conditioned form, and the qualities and relationships of that eternal being and the consequences of its eternal past must flow into the whole successional time-experience, metamorphosed into physical qualities, relationships and conditions. In the same way, when that successional experience is gathered together again into a region of timeless being, it is inevitable that it must be purged and fashioned so that it can form a real part of that eternal being. Moreover, it is equally obvious that, in preparing for a new existence, the eternal ego, together with the great beings that shape its destiny, should plan that the new life of successional time-experience should be such, as will enable the eternal being to get from it that development of being, which it needs for its ultimate perfection. It is upon these facts that the great reality of Karma depends.

Karma works into a new earth-life in consequence and metamorphosis in manifold ways: in the organic life of the body, in man's physical appearance, in his temperament, in his life of feeling, and in the circumstances which relate him to other beings and shape the main course of his life. It must be remembered, however, that the whole of this is the result of what the human spirit-being itself has recognised as essential, and has prepared for and assumed and faced, but which it has now, as such, forgotten, seeing its life only through its temporal physical consciousness.

Of course, not everything in this new life is the result of the Karma of the past life. There are many happenings which are creating new Karma for a future life, and there are happenings which are the result of other people's Karma crossing one's own life. But in its main lines, this life is the result of a previous existence and is the consequence of man being an eternal spirit.

This Karma we must face in freedom. As Dr. Wachsmuth writes in his book *Reincarnation*:

> We are not here faced, either with a previous predestination, in the sense of an external spiritual or natural compulsion, as has often been erroneously assumed; nor by an inner domination over the structure of destiny by a compulsory inter-relationship, as is often asserted by an uncomprehending astrology. We have, on the contrary, a free choice of the spiritual structure, the inner dynamics and the metamorphoses in the total course of our earth-life, which has been prepared beforehand in free participation with the beings of the spiritual world, in a state of higher consciousness.

Thus you have as Karmic factors in each earth-life the following:

1. The higher ego, with the individuality of its eternal spirit-being, as it has been fashioned through the whole course of its own spiritual and earthly evolution.
2. The soul characteristics and tendencies of its astral body, which are the result of its previous earth-life.
3. The formative forces of the etheric body, shaped by the deeds and thoughts of the previous earth-life, and working them out in a new life of successional time-existence.
4. The cosmically-prepared physical body worked upon continuously by the etheric body.
5. The selected hereditary qualities through the parents.
6. The chosen environment.

Modern science is only aware of numbers five and six, which it regards as only mechanically and materially conditioned. Yet by them alone it seeks to explain the whole human being and his life. Anthroposophy, however, being conscious of all these elements in the Karma of the individual being, realises that in them and in face of them the ego has to achieve its true freedom. As Rudolf Steiner wrote:

> From what is here manifest as Karma, man must indeed make himself increasingly free, *now*, in the age of physical consciousness. But the important matter is that he shall make himself free from it in the right way. With regard to these facts, we do not become free by denying them, or by simply accepting them, but only through a knowledge which enables us to acquire conscious control of them.

We must now consider the question of human Freedom in relation to Karma. In the first place let us remember that the physical world and physical consciousness are designed to enable the spirit to achieve the full development of its being in self-consciousness and freedom. All the conditions under which man lives serve this end. Now the ego in each one of us could never develop in this life—and certainly not in freedom—were it continuously aware of all the Karmic forces which are playing upon it. As Rudolf Steiner expresses it in one of his lectures:

> The earth-life is the opportunity of freedom, the opportunity of emancipating our souls from the necessities which bear relentlessly upon man in his spirit-existence. In the spirit-world man is imprisoned in this necessity of his being and its relationships. The world which surrounds him there takes hold of him as if he were hypnotised. He cannot look where he chooses as on earth, but he is, as it were, compelled to pay heed to the world about him in its full significance.

The earth existence, however, frees him from this in two directions. In the first place, while the physical world affects him in manifold ways, in his physical consciousness he is quite ignorant of its real being and of his true relationship to it. He perceives it only as an "appearance", that is, as it appears to his senses, and he is able to turn away, whenever he will, from his perception of it, and to act, to a large measure, independently of it.

Secondly, the manner of his earthly time-consciousness sets him free from the full consciousness and compulsion of his own being. The fact that man lives in our time-condition of past, present and future, may sometimes give him a feeling of frustration and disillusionment, but, because of this, he is not haunted by the reality of his past. His past seems to him something that no longer belongs to him, and, if he is to be held responsible for it, it can only be in some sort of relationship to "a deed done", and not to what is still part of his own being. At each present moment of his life he is able to make a choice, independently of the past which he feels he has left behind him, and of the future which does not yet belong to him. Thus we see that, in his earth-life, man feels more detached from his environment, and is, therefore, in a position to acquire for himself true freedom.

In regard to this, Rudolf Steiner reveals the great fact that the freedom of will which we seek is only to be won through the freedom of thought. We admit as much, in that we say, "I did it without thinking", and thereby imply that it was not a responsible or free act. Now, although, in comparison with our will, our thinking appears to us to be much more free, yet it is not completely free, because it is so largely dependent upon sense-experience. Even though man is not held in his earth-life in the inescapable necessity of thought which he would have to experience in the spirit-world, his thinking has yet to discover real freedom. This man will achieve, when he acquires the power of sense-free thinking. Christ's redeeming work for mankind is related directly to this freedom in which alone man can achieve his evolution, but this we shall consider in a separate chapter.

In our exposition of Rudolf Steiner's teaching about Reincarnation we have already met some of the difficulties which arise in men's minds today in regard to this belief. We have seen that the absence of the knowledge of reincarnation, especially among the western civilisations, was due to the gradual loss of spiritual vision and to man's increasing concentration upon the sense-phenomena of physical consciousness. We have also seen that the peoples of the East, and particularly of India, whose thinkers have always maintained a detached attitude towards sense-phenomena, have preserved the belief in reincarnation as it was taught in their ancient religion. It was, however, just because of their negative attitude towards man's earthly existence, that they did not rise to the full understanding of reincarnation. It was because they saw in the earth-life merely a doom to which man was subject and from which he escaped only in death, and to which he must perforce return because of his imprisonment in desire, that they regarded reincarnation merely as the turning of a wheel which brought man back to the same place. It was because of this that they saw history as the repetition of endless cycles of time, and did not have the progressive concept of it that has been significant of the west.

Rudolf Steiner combined the eastern awareness of the

spirit-world with the Western emphasis upon the importance of man's physical existence. In seeing the positive significance of man's earth-life as a fundamental element in the process of reincarnation, he makes the latter not a series of repeated cycles, but an ever-mounting spiral of evolution, leading through spiritual and earthly existences to a level of spirit-being, vastly higher than that which man possessed before he entered at all into an earthly existence.

We have also seen how man's gradual loss of the knowledge of his pre-earthly existence was a necessary condition of his ego-consciousness evolving in freedom. In the Eastern peoples who retained their belief in reincarnation, the development of ego-consciousness has lagged far behind that of the West, in which consciousness of pre-earthly existence became completely lost. It was for this reason that reincarnation did not appear as part of the teaching of Christianity, for the spiritual need of the awakening ego-consciousness in Western civilisation at that time was for an assurance of the continuance of its being in a future existence, and a sense of its own responsibility for endeavouring to secure that the goal of its earth-life should be reached. Man needed a "forward look" and would, therefore, have been impeded by a consciousness of the forces from a past life, playing into his present existence.

But man has passed through that stage and has arrived, in his knowledge of the world, at a highly-developed earthly ego-consciousness. The knowledge of reincarnation, which would once have impeded his progress, is now possible; indeed it is necessary for his future progress. He needs to discover that the ego is not to be found in isolation from, nor in opposition to, the objects of its experience, but in all the spiritual relationships which are part of its real being as a spirit. Moreover, unless he realises the truth of reincarnation and its implications, the wrong ideas which he possesses of his ego will be a very great obstacle to him in his own spiritual evolution after death.

Here too is the answer to those—and they are many—who feel that reincarnation, with its belief in a future life on earth in which there will be no direct memory of the present earth-life, implies the destruction of man's personality as he knows it here and now. In reply to this, it may well be asked what that level of personality is that only exists in the latest moment of a successional time-existence, and, for those who do not believe in a future existence, ends at death. The earthly life itself teaches us the importance, to the full make-up of personality, of experiences which have long passed out of memory. The youth or young man conceives of old age, with its loss of vigour, as a diminution of personality from which he shrinks, and he regards the passing of the years of his youth and strength as an irremediable loss. But in later years we are conscious that the experiences of our youth and early manhood, though largely forgotten, still play a great part in the formation of our personality and, in a measure, have not passed away.

Reincarnation, with its revelation that the past never fades out of existence, gives a deeper understanding of the true meaning of personality. We see that our youth could only form a permanent element in our personality by passing away in successional time, even to the extent of being almost completely forgotten. In this light we see our present earthly personality, not as arising out of a void, but as the expression of an eternal being, developing itself further by another life of earthly experience. We see, too, that no part of this life is lost, but that it is gathered up into that eternal self, But for this, it must pass away in earthly time. So too, when that eternal self shall express itself in yet another time-existence, the fruit of the former earth-life, though not present in the earthly memory at that time, will be working up in its karmic consequences, and bearing fruit in the development of the eternal self.

Finally, Reincarnation gives the answer to the universal problem, to which we have already referred, of lives handicapped from the start in body or circumstances, or cut off in childhood or in the early prime of life. It teaches us to bear in mind, in facing life's seemingly inexplicable tragic circumstances, the karmic consequences of past lives, and to realise that their significance and ultimate solution are not limited to this present existence. They no longer seem the tragic and hopeless denial of the possibility of any real earth-existence for the individual concerned.

In the words of Dr. Wachsmuth, "In the human being advancing through repeated births, there meet destiny, grace and freedom."[1]

[1] *Reincarnation*, p. 306.

CHAPTER XII

CHRIST AND MANKIND

We have on several occasions referred to the fact that, in the teaching of Steiner, the work of Christ is the central event both in human history and in the spiritual evolution of mankind. In this chapter we will try to deal with the matter more comprehensively. It would be a very remarkable thing—at the present time—to find a scientist who saw, in the relation of Christ to mankind, a central factor in human evolution and in the make-up of the human personality; or a historian who saw, in the life and death of Christ, the event which interprets all history before and after it. But that this should have happened in the first decade of this century was even less to be expected. That was a time when materialistic science was confidently assured of itself, when Protestant Christianity on the Continent was under the sway of the modernism of Harnack and Eucken, and was busy squaring Christian revelation with science. Even the Church of Rome at that time felt the breath of modernism. Great Britain was not so deeply affected by this as the Continent, but Anglican Christianity had settled into complacency, in its expectation of the new age of man promised by science. Christianity had lost its bite.

That at that very time Rudolf Steiner should have been expounding a spiritual interpretation of man's being and of human history, and should be putting the fact and work of Christ at the very centre of his explanations, is a remarkable phenomenon. It cannot be explained by Steiner's own past. Although in his childhood days in his country home he had had some contact with the services of his village church, he had been brought up in a free-thinking family, and neither at Vienna nor at Weimar had he taken any active part in the life of the Christian Church. Indeed he had been openly critical of the attitude of the Church towards the problem of faith and knowledge.

The only possible explanation lies in the spiritual revelation that came to his clairvoyant spirit at the close of the nineteenth century. It was the actual vision of the historical fact of the Mystery of Golgotha in the spirit-record of the Earth's history, that brought unquestioning conviction to Steiner's mind.

The further study of that record revealed to him the spiritual and historical relation of those facts of Christ's life to the whole evolution of man. He perceived that the life of Christ on earth is the culminating event of an age-long process, that reached back to that time in the spiritual beginning of human evolution, in which man was entangled in the Fall. The earliest consciousness in the mind of man of the coming of Christ appears in the Old Persian Civilisation, in the great revelation of Zarathustra concerning Ahura Mazdao, the God of Light, whom Zarathustra could see already descending towards the earth, in order to deliver man from the power of Ahriman. Steiner could see in the spirit-record how the expectation of the Christ appears again and again in the great religions of antiquity, through the teaching of the great Initiates, who in their mystery-clairvoyance were aware of his approach.

The actual coming of Christ to the Earth took place at the mid-most point of the evolution of the human soul, the point when it had reached its lowest descent from the spiritual to the material, and from which, by the Christ impulse, it began again to ascend to spirit-knowledge. As preparation for this coming, Steiner shows how the choice of the Hebrew nation, revealed in the Old Testament, was a necessary step in preparing a people who should have an ego-consciousness—albeit of the race and not yet of the individual—in advance of the rest of mankind, and who should thereby be able to receive the revelation of God, as the supreme divine Being, who stood in a direct personal relationship to them. Only a people so prepared could provide a body, in which could be manifest the supreme Ego-Being, the cosmic Christ. But

Steiner sees Christ as "the desire of all nations", the fulfilment, not only of the clear and conscious hope of the Jewish people, but of the dreams and longings of other nations, and of the hidden knowledge of the Initiates of the world. So too, he sees in the personality of Jesus of Nazareth the true Son of Man, the embodiment and meeting-place of all the spiritual streams of humanity.

With regard to the being of Christ Jesus, it is natural that as Steiner saw, through spirit-perception, a far greater mystery in the inter-relation of spirit and matter in the birth of man than is commonly understood, so he should see in the incarnation of Christ a mystery, even more strange and complex than its presentation in Christian theology. In considering this, it must always be borne in mind that Steiner only relates what he declares was manifest to him in the spiritual record. He is not enunciating a dogma, for in all the spiritual truths that he reveals, he declares again and again that nothing is to be regarded as dogmatic truth which *must* be accepted by a student of Anthroposophy. Indeed he warns the student that he must not credulously accept what he is told, but must test it with unprejudiced, rational judgment, until its truth becomes manifest to him.

When one realises all that reincarnation implies in the birth of an ordinary individual, it becomes clear that the Christ could not have been born in the normal way, if he were really to be the union of God with the true nature of man. For every man born into the world brings with him, in his physical organism of body and soul, the consequences of his former earth-lives. But Christ had never before been incarnate in human form, nor could he be incarnate in physical and etheric bodies made imperfect by the past influence of Lucifer and Ahriman. On the other hand, unless Christ Jesus contained in his being some relation to the fact and moral implication of reincarnation and Karma in the life of man, he could not be the Saviour of mankind.

Thus Steiner reveals in Jesus of Nazareth the union of two human streams, the sinless nature of the New-Adam, and the fullest and richest development of human nature through all the millennia of its reincarnating development. In so doing he gives the deepest significance to those seemingly contradictory elements in the nativity stories in the gospels of S. Matthew and S. Luke, which are for the most part disregarded or explained away in orthodox theology, and which, interpreted materialistically, are the grounds on which rational modernism disputes the truth of the recorded events.[1]

Steiner also reveals that it was not until his thirtieth year that Jesus was fully developed as Son of Man and that the eternal Christ-being entered into his physical body and united himself with it. This happened at the baptism in Jordan. This was a widely held view in the early Church, and is expressed in the Epistle to the Hebrews in the quotation from the fortieth psalm, "A body didst thou prepare for me! Then said I, Lo, I am come to do thy will." However, through a materialistic conception of reality, this view led to heresies in which the true union of the divine and human natures in Christ Jesus was denied. In consequence, the point in earthly time at which the Christ actually entered into the physical nature of Jesus was put back to his birth and even to his conception.

Once again, however, let us recall the process of reincarnation in every human individual, the pre-conception preparation of his being in the spirit-world, the inherited physical life from the parents, the infant growing, at first apart from the spiritual ego that is soon to dwell in it, and then the entry of the ego into the physical being of the child and its gradual development in its three bodies to its final evolution; and, finally, in the first decade of its adult life, its self-expression in its own individual experience of the world. In this whole process man becomes incarnate. In the same way we realise that in the whole of the mysterious and, at first reading, apparently complex process of the Incarnation of Christ described to us by Steiner, beginning with the act of divine

[1] We have only here given an indication of Steiner's account of the birth and childhood of Jesus of Nazareth. A detailed account and explanation is given in his writings. See *The Gospel of St. Luke* and *From Jesus to Christ*. It can only be understood and judged in relation to the being and evolution of Man as revealed in Spiritual Science.

initiative, spoken of in the Annunciation, right up to the spirit-event recorded in the Gospel at the Baptism in Jordan, we have the single spiritual event of the Incarnation of Christ into the being of Man. For we remember how the whole process of human rebirth is prepared for and watched over by the pre-earthly human ego, aided by exalted spirit beings, long before the ego itself indwells or has expressed itself in the physical organism. So this whole process of Incarnation is the work of Christ Himself, working out of the spirit-world, aided and served by other beings, earthly and heavenly.

Here we confront a profound truth in regard to the spiritual and the physical, the eternal and the temporal, the failure to understand which has been the cause of most of the apparent contradictions in earthly existence, and of the bitterest disputes in the interpretation of events that have divided mankind.

The truth is this. "An eternal spiritual reality can only be expressed in temporal physical existence *as a process*." Man has become used to limiting reality to the present moment of his conscious contact with his ever-changing material environment. In that "present" reality he sees the consequence or effect of the past, and the germ or potentiality of the future. But the actual happenings of the past and that which will become manifest physical reality in the future are, to ordinary consciousness, neither of them at the moment "real". Reality for the ordinary man exists only at every moment of successional existence.

Of purely material objects, as such, this is true, but in regard to any spiritual reality expressed in them, it is not true. We have already seen the false conception of his own being and of the nature of his earthly existence which has arisen in man from this conception, and how the first experience of higher knowledge is that the whole earthly sequence of successive events are seen to be a single entity in a continuous-time existence.

It is because of this false conception of reality that men have disputed at what point in successional earthly time Christ was incarnate in Jesus, and have held that at whatever time in the earthly life of Jesus this took place, then, before that moment the Incarnation had not begun, and Jesus was a mere man. But, as a spiritual happening, the Incarnation is inherent, as one event, in the whole earthly process, from the Annunciation to the Ascension. It is only in the light of this truth about spiritual reality that we can understand the words: "the Lamb slain from the foundation of the world."

More than this cannot be said in this short chapter. The Mystery of the Incarnation of Christ revealed by Rudolf Steiner needs to be studied in its wholeness and with a true understanding of the spiritual evolution of mankind, in order to be understood. It is enough, for the moment, to say that in Jesus of Nazareth, preaching, dying and rising again, as recorded in the Gospels, Steiner sees the Son of God, the cosmic Christ, incarnate in a Man who expresses in himself the whole race of mankind.

The Mystery of Golgotha, the death of Christ upon the Cross, is the subject of many books and lectures by Steiner, and he sees in it the one act that worked the salvation of mankind. Here again we have to note that the knowledge of the fact of reincarnation, the discovery that man is a spirit-being, evolving through alternating physical and spiritual lives, necessitates a new interpretation of the problem of human salvation and of the redemptive work of Christ. Christ came, as the New Testament explicitly tells us, to save the souls of men. Steiner reveals how men's souls were in two ways in desperate need of such salvation. In the first place the concentration of human thought on man's material existence, with its definite conclusion at death, had led him so to identify the life of his soul with that earthly experience, that he was coming to doubt the reality of any existence for his soul after death. Moreover, by reason of that very doubt, man's soul was in even greater peril in its existence after death. For in the soul-world of purgation, man's soul was becoming earth-bound in its earth-experience, and was unable, in its spirit-blindness, to find the Christ, who had once been the leader of the souls of men through that region out into the pure spirit-world. The Bible speaks of such souls as "spirits in prison", and reveals that, after his death on the

Cross, Christ descended into this world of imprisoned souls, in a form in which they could recognise him, and revealed to them the way and the means by which they could emerge from bondage to their earth-existence, into the higher levels of the spirit-world.[1]

Out of his own spirit perception Rudolf Steiner declared that we cannot fulfil our tasks as human beings after death with the right consciousness, if we have not taken the Christ spirit into ourselves during our earthly life. "We live towards a future", he once said, "in which men will deprive themselves more and more of the possibility of living in the right way in the time between death and a new birth, if they alienate themselves from the Christ Event."

In the Mystery of Golgotha, the death and resurrection of Jesus Christ, Steiner sees the defeat of Ahriman and Lucifer, the deliverance of mankind from the power of sin and from the fear of death, the restoration to him of the certain hope of immortality for his soul, and the pledge of his recovery of his lost spiritual nature.

In a special way Steiner sees in Christ's deed the "taking away of the sin of the world", the deliverance of the Earth, as a spirit-entity, from the corrupting influence of the age-long sin of man, present in the spiritual record of the Earth itself. Christ restored to the Earth, which Ahriman had almost subdued to his materialistic purpose, the possibility of ultimately fulfilling God's purpose for it, as the sphere of man's spiritual evolution. This was a cosmic redemption, quite beyond the power of man to achieve. It was the divine defeat of the ultimate purpose of Evil, and the implanting of a new all-conquering Impulse into human evolution.

In a very special way Steiner related the Mystery of Golgotha to the great Mysteries of the past, whose historical function he has revealed as that of meeting the problem of man's loss of connection with his spirit-origin, by revealing to man spiritual truth, and by initiating certain men to a direct knowledge of the spirit-world. He saw in the Mystery of Golgotha a great Mystery-event. In the Ancient Mysteries

[1] See I Peter iii. 19 and S. John v. 28.

chosen and prepared men were initiated, one by one, in the secrecy of the Mystery-temple, into the certain knowledge of their spirit-origin. In the Mystery of Golgotha, in visible deeds of human history, Christ made possible, for all mankind, an initiation into the recovery of their spiritual nature and their spiritual destiny.

In the ancient Mysteries man had to dissociate himself from his physical consciousness and lift himself to a higher level of consciousness, in order that he might make contact with the Divine. To do this, the Master Initiate had partially to raise the etheric body of the candidate out of its connection with his physical body, so that the vision of his spirit nature might for ever be imprinted on his memory. But man, in the days of Christ, had reached the stage in his evolution in which the etheric body was completely immersed in the physical body, and it was no longer possible safely to raise it out of it. The rite of Baptism, with its total immersion in water, was the latest—and more physical—means of securing a momentary detachment of the etheric from the physical. But to most people in the first century, even that experience was no longer really possible, and the rite was becoming a symbol, like the other traditional mystery rites in the Mysteries themselves. The way back to actual knowledge of the Divine world was barred.

In Christ, the Divine descended to the level of physical consciousness in which man was bound. There it could now be found and known. Moreover, man's daily earthly life, which seemed to him that which led him away from the spiritual, was to be the way which led to it. Christ rescued man's earthly life from the power of Lucifer and Ahriman, and hallowed it to be a daily path to God. He called to men to follow him, and he revealed to them the moral and spiritual laws of the "kingdom", the spirit-world, so that they might know how to live on earth rightly as spirit-beings. Even the sorrow, sin and suffering of the world were part of that pathway to the spirit, and finally death itself was revealed, not as the negation of man's spiritual hope, but as the gateway to eternal life.

But it was not enough for Christ to call to men to follow Him to the spirit-world lying beyond the span of this earth-life. They needed a new ego; their earth-bound ego could not tread this path. In New Testament language "they must be born again". This is a spiritual truth. Let us try to come to a factual understanding of it. Man's conception of himself, bounded and conditioned by successional earth-experience, is quite different from his ego-consciousness, when he finds himself, after death, faced with the fact of his eternal being, and with the whole continuous living tableau of his earth-experience, as part of his being. For we have seen how, then, he immediately sees his earth-experience in a new moral light, and stands in judgment upon himself—and how he needs a period of purgation and self-adjustment, before he can function as his higher self in higher worlds.

Now the initiate into the Mysteries received that impression of his true eternal self in his initiation, and brought it back with him for ever into his physical consciousness. He had become a new man. He was called "twice-born". But man could no longer tread the path of Mystery-initiation, and his earth-bound ego-consciousness was far more overwhelming than it had been in ancient days. It was not enough for Christ to tell men that the earthly path itself could be the path to heaven: men had to be changed; they had to become the sort of men who could so tread that earthly path.

So Christ wrought for mankind what the Mysteries had done for men of old. He gave them a knowledge of their true higher self. He did not give it to them once and for all in a single vision, but day by day in an ever-deepening certainty, in a daily awareness of the spirit-world. Through the Mystery of Golgotha Christ aroused in man's soul love and devotion to himself, and he so united his soul-life with their own, that he awoke in them a consciousness of his real presence within them. In this consciousness of the indwelling presence of Christ, the Christian became aware of the true nature of his own being, and felt that his old lower self was being changed. He felt that he was "a new man in Christ". No longer did he feel that his soul was hopelessly bound up with his physical existence; indeed, he felt that he was already freed from it. In this union with Christ there awoke in him the life of the Spirit, which became for him the victory over sin and death in his own life. S. Paul called it "the first-fruits of our inheritance", "Christ in us, the hope of glory". On this experience he based his own certainty of immortality. "Nothing again can ever separate me from the love of God, which is in Christ Jesus, my Lord." From that day until now, through all the vicissitudes of history, the indwelling presence of Christ has been for Christians, the real initiation of man's earthly ego into the spirit world, the recovery within himself of his higher ego. "I live; yet not I, but Christ liveth in me."

This relationship of the Mystery of Golgotha to the ancient Mysteries was so plain to Steiner, that within a year or two of his direct vision at the beginning of the century he wrote his book, *Christianity as Mystical Fact*. But the Christian initiation of man's ego, Steiner declares, is not yet complete. There is a third initiation into the spirit which Christ has made possible for mankind. It is the initiation of man's *thinking* into spirit-knowledge. Only now has that third initiation become possible, and only through Christ can it be truly achieved. But of this we must speak in the next chapter.

CHAPTER XIII

THE INITIATION OF THINKING

We have seen in our account of Steiner's life and in what we have already set out of his teaching, what a strong emphasis he laid upon thinking. He had himself, in direct experience, found in thought the doorway into the perception of the spirit-world. He had discovered, in the evolution of sense-free thinking, the one means whereby he could understand and relate together his experience of different levels of supersensible knowledge, and apply to it, at every level, conscious, rational judgment. Moreover, in discovering the new powers and possibilities of thinking as an instrument of knowledge, he had also discovered in it functions of which man had lost all knowledge. He had discovered that it operated as creative, formative forces in the life of man, both in the spiritual and physical worlds, a creative function which in a way was more primary to it than its function as the instrument of human knowledge. Aristotle, over two thousand years ago, had so defined the working of Thought in the human organism, as primarily creative, and secondarily, reflective. Modern thinking has not attached much significance to this definition. It remained for Steiner to discover, in spirit-perception, the factual truth of Aristotle's description—and in doing so, he penetrated to some of the deepest secrets in the being of man.

Indeed, in nothing is Rudolf Steiner more outstanding than in his understanding and exposition of the nature of thinking and of its evolution in the history of mankind. Some points in regard to this we have touched upon already, but it is so fundamental and important, that it is worth while making a comprehensive review of the whole subject. In doing so, we shall see it, as Steiner saw it from first to last, in its relation to the redemption work of Christ.

In speaking of the history of thought, we generally conceive of it as the faculty of conscious reflective human thinking, such as, in its more complete form, expresses itself in philosophy. In his *History of Western Philosophy*, Bertrand Russell takes Thales who lived in the sixth century B.C., as the first of the philosophers. One might well wonder how it can be held that the history of thought began in the sixth century, when one thinks of the profound spiritual and metaphysical writings of the ancient religions of India and Egypt, and of the great civilisations of Babylonia.

In a real sense, however, it may be said that the history of thought begins with Thales, for with him man began to have a completely new attitude towards thought. In the ancient world man regarded thoughts as realities that were given to him out of the spiritual world, realities which had a spirit-existence of their own of which he was made aware. We have already pointed out in the chapter on the evolution of mankind, that as man lost his spirit-perception, and as his consciousness of his experience of the physical world grew, it appeared to him, more and more, that his thoughts arose out of his own mind.[1] With that consciousness began the evolution of thought as man now conceives of it.

The earlier Greek scientific philosophers were still aware, through participation in the traditional teaching of the Mysteries, of the elemental realities of earth, water, air and fire, as the basis of the physical world, and constructed, out of the working of their awakening thinking upon this knowledge, a scientific concept of the universe. Thus, Heraclitus was still aware of the reality of constant movement and change in the etheric world, and based upon it his concept of the universe in the words, "Everything is in movement". Gradually, however, this lingering mystery knowledge passed away, and we come to the Greek thought of the fifth and fourth centuries, which was concerned with the problems of the life of man in the world of sense-experience. In all directions man's own creative powers blossomed out, in drama, in architecture, in art, and in politics; and there arose a distrust of the authority of revealed truth. Soon, however, as men no longer filled the wells of their knowledge from spiritual fountains, they

[1] See pp. 108, 111.

began to dry up, and in the middle of the century we have the Sophists of Athens, engaged in an exchange of brilliant, but empty, cleverness.

At this moment there began that amazing century of Greek philosophy, in Socrates, Plato and Aristotle. The great task of Socrates was to teach men to think for themselves, deeply and truly. He knew that the sources of direct spirit-knowledge were drying up in the Mysteries, of which he was an initiate, and that man would have to depend, more and more, on the apparently self-derived thought of his own mind, and he was concerned to teach men how to use that great, new-born faculty accurately and sincerely.

Plato, expounding the teaching of his beloved master, and uniting the power of Socratic thought to what he could still behold of spirit-reality, created a philosophy as noble and profound as any the world has ever seen.

When, in the second half of the fourth century we come to Aristotle, the pupil of Plato, we come to a world in which man was already taking a far wider interest in the whole of his physical surroundings. Plato's philosophy had been concerned almost entirely with the problems of man's personal, social, and political conduct, but Aristotle's writings range also over the whole field of natural history. With far less direct perception of the spirit-world than Plato had, but still with the certainty of a spirit background to the universe, Aristotle realised that, if man's knowledge was to conquer his physical environment, he must no longer base it on any supersensible revelation or tradition, but entirely upon the structure of his own mind. He produced a system of logic, based on the laws of the working of man's mind in relation to sense-observation, which for the next eighteen centuries was the canon of all human thinking.

After Aristotle, all conception of the reality of the spiritual faded and the fountain of philosophical inspiration dried up into an agnostic philosophy of conduct, based either upon the personal pride of the Stoic, or upon the realistic materialism of the Epicurean. The world, too, was now under the domination of the Romans, to whom power meant more than philosophy, and who borrowed the thinking of the conquered Greeks as an adjunct to their own love of power. It became, as we have seen, a world, in which man could have no confidence in his higher instincts, nor faith in his spiritual future.

At this moment of human need Christ came to the world, and his coming was prepared for in an almost unnoticed manner. Roman conquest had brought from the East a wave of mysticism, which maintained itself against the scepticism of Western thought by a withdrawal from the world into a communal monastic life. This movement began in the second century B.C., and in the Therapeutæ of Egypt and the Essenes of Palestine it reached a high level. When the new seed of Christianity was sown in the Roman world, it took special root in this spiritual substratum. Out of it sprang the Christian hermitic and monastic movements. Moreover, the direct spiritual initiation which Christ had bestowed on his earliest followers, and which is evidenced in certain of the "gifts of the Spirit" in the New Testament, united itself, in some measure, with the clairvoyant perception and mystic speculation of this new Gnosticism.

Later, on Gnosticism began to permeate the philosophic thinking against whose scepticism it had originally been a protest, and under its influence philosophy turned back to its spiritual sources in Plato, and, in the third century, produced Neoplatonism, one of the most spiritually and intellectually profound systems of philosophy the world has ever seen. In its leader, Plotinus, supersensible perception soared to a higher level than even the spirit-perception of Plato had reached.

The Christian thought of the first three centuries was caught up into this movement, and sought to see the mysteries of the Christian revelation against this background of spirit knowledge. Sometimes it had to resist its aberrations, sometimes, as in its great leaders, Clement and Origen, it draws inspiration from its soaring spiritual understanding.

During the fourth and fifth centuries this reawakening of spirit knowledge died away again. For Gnosticism, for all its recovery of ancient spirit-vision and its exalted concept of Christ as the divine spirit-being descending from the heavens, was quite unable to grasp the spiritual necessity and fact of his incarnation into human form. Gnosticism was therefore condemned as a heresy and, later, was ruthlessly exterminated. With the adoption of Christianity as the state religion, and the imperial demand that it should shape its theology into an ordered uniformity, and with the banishment from the Empire of the Neoplatonic philosophers, the world settled down again into a sense-bound thinking, united in the Christian Church with a divine revelation. In such a world the Christian out-thought the Pagan, and there arose the majestic figure of Augustine, who saw in the Incarnation of Christ the visible manifestation of the profound philosophical mysteries of Plotinus.

Then came the crash of the Roman Empire and, in a sense, the evolution of thought began over again. As we have seen there was already in the Germanic tribes a spirit-consciousness that looked forwards rather than backwards, and which adapted itself fairly easily to the Christian revelation. The thinking of this new European civilisation was dictated at this stage by the theology of the Christian Church, and by the formal logic of Aristotle. It was all that remained to Europe of his vast teaching.

A subterranean stream of spiritual thought from Plotinus burst up once or twice in those dark ages, but it was not until the twelfth and thirteenth centuries that the impetus of the Crusades and the impact of Arabian philosophy created a situation, in which Thomas Aquinas rose to a height of spiritual perception, both in philosophy and theology, that lifted thought again to the level of Origen and Plotinus. In this philosophy, the ever-increasing ego-consciousness of man in his thinking was checked by the recognition of the overriding authority of revelation.

Meanwhile, the individualistic, sense-directed consciousness of the Germanic peoples was awakening and, quickened by the recovery of the greater part of Aristotle's writings in the Renaissance, it burst into an independence of thinking which heralded the new age. Within two centuries of the death of Thomas Aquinas, the age of sense-derived human thinking, which neither concerned itself with the content of revelation nor would brook its control, was firmly established. The mood of the age expressed itself in the words of Francis Bacon in the seventeenth century: "Reality only presents itself to us when we look out upon the world of the senses. The senses alone provide us with realities, the realities of empirical knowledge." The age of Science, the age of inductive reason based on sense-observation, had begun. By the nineteenth century it possessed the field. Philosophy had been thrust on one side, and an attack was being made on the content of revelation, on the assumption that it could rightly be judged by sense-derived thinking.

A protest was made in Goethe's spiritual concept of Nature, and in Hegel's apotheosis of pure thought. But neither of them could carry his conclusions into the realm of actual spirit-reality, and on a side-issue Hegel was made the justification of Marxian Communism and of nationalistic political totalitarianism, both of which have brought mankind to the present impasse.

The latest reaction against these tyrannies is Existentialism, partly the expression of philosophical thinking, partly the reaction of humanity, outraged by the totalitarian suppression of the individual. But Existentialism either reverts to the certainties of revealed religion, with Marcel, or to the nihilism of Sartre, which wrings its hands—or else laughs in derision—over the futility of exercising the freedom of will of the human individual, which it has been driven to assert. At best we are still in a situation in which reason and faith must be content to function in different spheres. Neither of them has the expectation of the power of direct perception of spirit-reality, and neither of them regards the visible world as the immediate expression of spirit-activity.

Yet it is this very experience that Steiner declares is available to man today, by raising his powers of thinking from bondage to sense-experience into direct perception of supersensible reality. It is to this goal of spirit ego-consciousness, he declares, that Christ is leading mankind at this moment. The pathway is open to man, but only by the initiation of Christ himself can man safely venture upon it.

We have seen how, in the days of Christ's life on earth, when man had in his sense-bound experience lost, beyond recovery, the consciousness of his pre-earthly ego, Christ, by indwelling in his heart in love and devotion, filled him with the consciousness of a higher self, that he knew was not himself, but Christ in him. In this way Christian faith and worship nursed and directed the evolution of the ego-consciousness of European man, right up to the age of reason. Now, after four centuries of development of scientific thought, man has very largely lost his faith in spiritual revelation, and, having bound himself in a far more extensive, and also a far more materialistic, world-concept, can still find no consciousness of his own ego that is not bounded by his sense-experience. For such a sense-bound, egotistic ego-consciousness to penetrate suddenly into the realm of spirit-reality, could only produce a tragedy such as that of Nietzsche. Only that individual who, in consciousness of the indwelling of Christ, has begun to experience in himself the awakening of his own true spirit-ego, can safely venture into the direct knowledge of the spirit-world.

Two thousand years ago, Christ initiated human feeling and devotion into faith in the spirit-world and in the reality of man's spirit-destiny, and so made possible the evolution of his ego-consciousness and the development of his powers of thought. Today he would make possible for him the recovery in clear knowledge and understanding of his true spirit-heritage, by initiating his thinking into direct spirit-experience. The redemption of human thinking is the completion of the spirit-initiation of mankind by Christ.[1]

Steiner expresses, in one of his lectures, the centrality of Christ in the world-picture revealed by Spiritual Science:

> For those who will lift themselves to Initiation Science, there opens-up, as they rise from Inspiration to Intuition, a spiritual world, which contains the Mystery of Golgotha, like the mighty consolation within the whole world's existence.

[1] For a much fuller treatment of this subject, see *The Redemption of Thinking—a Study in the Philosophy of Thomas Aquinas*, by Rudolf Steiner, translated and edited by A. P. Shepherd and Mildred Robertson Nicoll. (To be published shortly.)

CHAPTER XIV

SPIRITUAL SCIENCE AND MODERN THOUGHT

So far we have presented an outline of the teaching of Rudolf Steiner in regard to the nature and evolution of Man and the Universe. We have also shown that he sets this out, not as a theory, but as the result of direct observation of real phenomena, although they are phenomena which are not discernible by the physical senses. What he presents is *Spiritual Science*, that is to say a scientific account of the phenomena which lie behind sense-perception. Our next step must be to relate this Spiritual Science to modern thought, to consider what fresh concepts of knowledge it may bring to it, and how far it challenges, or sheds new light upon, its conclusions.

In attempting to do this we must once again ask the reader to clear his mind of all prejudice, for it is characteristic of modern thought to assume, either that supersensible phenomena have no real existence, or that any attempt to describe such an existence or to base knowledge upon it, must be unscientific. Many distinguished thinkers today are challenging such an attitude. In his book, *Living Time*, the late Dr. Maurice Nicoll writes:

> One point about materialism, as regards its limiting effect upon man, would seem to lie in the attitude it takes towards the existence of higher degrees of reality. Man's reason is taken to be capable of attaining to a complete knowledge of the laws and the nature of all things. His consciousness, while it is capable of including more and more *facts*, is not regarded as capable of attaining a new *quality*. Higher degrees of consciousness and higher degrees of truth and entirely new forms of experience are excluded.

But is the sole method of experiencing or understanding life by way of the method of science? Is not science merely one mode of experience? Are not further states of consciousness most likely to be the key to the understanding of the complexities and contradictions that have arisen in the realm of physics?

The detailed application of the teaching of Spiritual Science to the methods and conclusions of modern thought would cover a field far too vast to attempt in such a book as this. Indeed, it is a task which can only be undertaken by those who have first-hand knowledge in the various departments of modern thought. All that can be done here is to attempt to give some of the immediate and most obvious results of applying these new ideas.

But before we attempt to do this, let us remind ourselves how repeatedly Rudolf Steiner disclaimed any intention of disparaging or denying the achievements of modern scientific thought. He acclaimed and admired them, and the mental and moral qualities which produced them. He presented Anthroposophy as an equally serious and factually-perceived science of the world outside sense-experience—a world from which modern thought has locked itself out—and, as such, he invited the modern world to consider this science of the supersensible and relate it to its own world-concept.

Let us begin by recalling the main factors in the world-outlook presented by Spiritual Science. The first and most important of these is the assertion of the spiritual nature of the universe, that man is not set in an indifferent, material environment, but in a universe of intelligent spirit-beings, working in a way consonant with the freedom and spiritual evolution of mankind. While the material phenomena of the world are governed by the fixed principles of natural law, this law is itself maintained and activated by spirit-beings.

The second factor is the account of the spiritual origin of man and the universe, and their evolution from a condition of pure spirit-being to their present material form.

The third factor concerns the earthly history of mankind.

It asserts that man, as an earthly being, has not always been possessed of the same faculties, progressing in the development of them only in the process of acquiring mastery of his material environment. Man's being has evolved through the atrophy of some faculties and the development of others, through a spiritual descent and an intellectual ascent, from a primitive, direct consciousness of the spirit-background of himself and the universe and an ignorance of the material world, to an ever-increasing material knowledge and skill and a complete loss of spirit-awareness. His future evolution points to a re-ascent to spiritual knowledge, in the power of his developed faculties of physical perception and understanding.

The fourth assertion is that man, as an individual being, is not merely the creation of that particular stage of human earthly evolution, at which he may happen to live. He is an eternal spirit-being, having his existence in an alternating rhythm of spiritual and earthly lives, related with one another in a process of moral consequence, that is to say, by the laws of his own eternal being.

The fifth factor is that, behind the material phenomena of the sense-world, including the physical organism of man, there is a world of formative forces, imperceptible by the physical senses, but objectively perceptible at the first level of higher consciousness as giving life, movement and form to the material world. This is called "the etheric world".

Sixthly—and of vital importance—this etheric world functions under the conditions of continuous, and not successional, time. Every event in the etheric world and in its working upon the material world, remains in a continuous time-relationship to the events which, in successional time, preceded or followed it, and, as such, is perceptible, and available to re-experience at the level of higher consciousness. While the material realities of the physical world pass out of existence, the spirit pattern that produced and underlies them survives, and the visible psychic representation of each event remains, and is recoverable as a psychic experience by higher knowledge. Thus anyone who has raised his consciousness to that level is able to survey and even to re-experience the past.

Conceptions such as these cannot but have a profound effect upon the conclusions of modern knowledge. In the first place, in the sphere of *Natural Science*, they challenge at once the generally-accepted scientific theory of the origin of man and the universe. Man, it is seen, has not evolved out of the lower forms of animal existence, which themselves have arisen out of the most elementary form of matter. There has been a kind of dual evolutionary process. On the one hand, there has been the evolution of the material world towards a condition in which man could live as a physical being; and, on the other hand, man's whole organism has been evolved, by the activity of spirit-beings, to the stage at which he could consciously function in a material body. These two evolutionary processes, as it were, converged, until they united at the point where man's spirit-being, his ego, could be incarnate in material form. The animal world consists of beings which have entered into material form at an earlier stage at which their real spirit-being could not incarnate, and are therefore incapable of spirit-development. While man existed in spirit form before the animal world, he was the last to descend into a material form.[1] This would explain why there is no trace of man in the earliest fossil remains.

Moreover, the preservation of form in a species, and also its variation or "mutation", are seen to be neither mechanical

[1] "The present animals are beings who have, as it were, remained behind at earlier stages of evolution, who have preserved those earlier stages of evolution and hardened them. Man has grown out beyond his earlier stages of development; the animal has grown down beneath them. Thus in the animal world we see, as it were, brothers of humanity, who have remained behind, but who no longer bear the form of those earlier stages of evolution. For those earlier stages took their course in an age when the conditions of life on earth were different, when the elements were not yet distributed as they are today, when man was not yet burdened with a body such as he has today—and yet was man. In the course of evolution man was able to wait, if we may use this image. He was able to delay his entry into the flesh until a later time—until this fleshy material could evolve in such a way that man might develop the power of his present mind and spirit. The animals were not able to wait; they became hardened at an earlier stage. They entered into the flesh before the proper time—hence they had to remain behind."—Lecture on *Spiritual Science, Christianity and the Future of Mankind* by Rudolf Steiner.

nor accidental. Once one realises the active spirit background of the physical world, the discovery of the physical organ of heredity and of the fact that it is built up out of "genes", is seen as a discovery of the process by which spirit-activity expresses itself physically in securing the general uniformity of a species, or, by a deliberate rearrangement of the structure of a gene, in producing a mutation in the species. Each species obviously manifests an adaptation of the form of the species beneath it, but the variation has not arisen out of the lower species. It is a conscious adaptation of the form of the lower species by spirit-beings, in order to make it the medium of a higher spiritual incarnation, made possible, in many instances, by a development in the evolution of the material environment.

Moreover, Spiritual Science reveals that man is subject to two other processes of evolution besides that of his physical organism. In the first place he is subject, in the life of the race and in his own individual earth life, to an evolutionary process in his soul-consciousness, which manifests itself in his gradually increasing awareness of the functioning of his own spirit-being through the different "bodies", astral, etheric and physical, of his earthly organism.

Finally, he is subject, as an eternal spirit-individual, to a process of moral and spiritual evolution in the rhythm of his own individual existence, through alternating physical and spiritual conditions of being. Thus Spiritual Science reveals evolution as a far more complicated and far-reaching process in Man and the Universe, than that assumed by natural science. An application of the revealed facts of Spiritual Science to the principle of evolution has been worked out, in close relationship to embryology, by Dr. Hermann Poppelbaum, in his book *Man and Animal.*

We quoted Dr. Maurice Nicoll's claim that science is only one mode of experience and has no right to declare impossible higher levels of consciousness. But these levels, once reached, belong to science just as much as to any other department of human thought. It is *to a new way of thinking* that Spiritual Science challenges modern thought. A century and a half ago Goethe proclaimed a new way of scientific thinking, which concentrated upon the whole, rather than upon the part, on the form, rather than on the ultimate constituent elements of the material substance. It was a method which required infinite patience and humility on the part of the scientific observer, and an imaginative capacity to unite his whole being with the thing observed. Goethe could not carry the method to its full exposition, and as it could not produce such quick results and such immediately practical discoveries as the analytic, atomistic method of the impersonal observer and experimenter, it was brushed aside. It has remained for Rudolf Steiner to develop Goethe's method to the direct experience of the spirit-realities implicit in sense-phenomena, and to a rational exposition of the new conditions of thought and experience involved in them. He makes the claim that if the scientist will make the effort to rise to this new level of experience, or will adopt these new ways of thought as a hypothesis, he will discover for himself vast new fields of knowledge. Two books have recently been published which apply these new methods of thinking to scientific problems and conclusions, and open up new lines of scientific exploration.[1]

When we turn to the study of *History*, it is obvious that the main principles of the teaching of Spiritual Science that we have set out will correct a number of the assumptions of historians, and shed much light upon some historical problems. The primary assertion that man's primitive consciousness was a clairvoyant perception of a spirit-environment of which he was a part, and by which he was guided and taught, is a challenge to the usual conception of man, as painfully arising, under the pressure of biological and environmental necessities, out of an animal consciousness. It places right back, at the most primitive stage of human civilisation, an awareness of certain personal relationships, and it explains the spiritual profundity of some of of the earliest religious beliefs.

Furthermore, the fact that as general clairvoyance declined,

[1] *Man or Matter*, by Ernest Lehrs. Faber. *The Plant between Sun and Earth*, by George Adams and Olive Whicher.

Mystery-centres were formed by leading spiritual personalities, at which selected individuals were prepared and trained in clairvoyant perception, and that these Mystery-initiates, by their perception of the spirit-background of the physical world, became the teachers and leaders in the acquisition and development of civilised arts and practices, is again a matter of profound historical importance. It places the origin of civilisation in a revealed knowledge of the relation between the material and the spiritual, and not in a groping biological or environmental urge. It also explains the existence of the ancient priest-king.

Animism is seen to be, not the universal beginning of all civilisations, but a state of deterioration, where the ancient clairvoyance has degenerated, without the presence of a Mystery-centre to teach and guide it. It is noteworthy that where the spiritual guidance of the Mysteries was missing, material civilisation hardly developed. The loss of clairvoyance invariably begins with the loss of awareness of the highest spiritual beings, and finally results in a consciousness of only the lower, elemental and, indeed, sub-human spirits. For example, in the Greek-Asiatic communities of the Eastern Empire in the days of Christ, when spiritual clairvoyance, where it survived, was at its lowest ebb, the phenomenon of demon-possession as described in the New Testament was far worse and more widespread than in earlier centuries. S. Paul, in his letters to the Galatians, speaks of their pre-Christian life as having been "subject to the beggarly elemental-spirits, who were no real gods". It is an almost universal belief in animistic African tribes, that there was once a time when men knew the mighty, beneficent spirits, who have now abandoned them.

Again, Myths are seen in a new light as a stage in the loss of clairvoyance. They are first a memory, and then a dramatisation, of the "picture-consciousness" of the lowest level of clairvoyant perception. They are not imaginary conceptions, derived to explain the physical universe—an abstract achievement quite impossible to that level of human development. They are a picture-experience of man's soul-relationship to his spiritual and earthly environment. They are revelations of his soul-evolution.[1]

Again, the revelation that primitive clairvoyance, as an experience of etheric reality, was a continuous time experience, is of the greatest importance in interpreting primitive history. For in such etheric experience the past is always recoverable. The beginning of written records is usually taken as marking a very early stage in the evolution of the human mind. But while man had clairvoyant perception of the past, *the need of written records did not exist.* Moreover, even when clairvoyance diminished, the Mystery-Initiates could always recover and relate the past. It would only be with the almost complete disappearance of clairvoyance and the decadence of the Mysteries, that the need of written records would arise. This fact reveals the mistake of dating the origin of the ancient religions of India and Persia by the earliest written records of them, in about the sixth century B.C. For in religion the Mystery-centres would make the need of written records not only unnecessary, but undesirable, lest sacred truth should fall into unhallowed possession.

A great initiate, such as Moses, would, by his acquired higher knowledge, be able to look back into the most distant human past. The earliest chapters of Genesis must not be taken as an imaginary description of creation—their brevity and sublimity would almost contradict that. They are "Imaginations", the picture-images in the clairvoyant perception of the past, which visualise the great stages in the evolution of the physical universe. As such they were directly recoverable by Moses, "learned in all the wisdom of the Egyptians".

We have already seen, in presenting Steiner's own account of the spiritual evolution of human consciousness, how this evolution of human consciousness explains and relates organic-

[1] cf. Nicholas Berdyaev. "I wish to deny the current identification of myth with invention and make-believe; with anything, in fact which is contrary to reality. I see the greatest realities, the original phenomena of spiritual life, concealed in the myths of mankind—realities that are more concrete than the concepts and ideas of discursive reason."—*Dream and Reality*, p. 181.

ally the great civilisations of the past, and we have traced it in the evolution of thought in Western civilisation. It can be traced in the history of every age and people, in the rise and fall of every civilisation. So too, the appearance of great creative human personalities, which Professor Toynbee sees as one of the great factors in human history, is clearly understood in the light of Reincarnation.

Another historical problem that is engaging the minds of historians today is the question as to whether a moral pattern is discernible in the historical process. "Judgment," says Professor Butterfield, "is embedded in the very constitution of the universe, embedded in the fabric of history." Here again the fact of the persistence of events in a continuous-time relationship, and the realisation that the historical life of every individual is set in the background of an eternal, continuous existence integrated by moral law, reveals morality at the very heart of history.

In all these directions the teachings of Spiritual Science throw light and interpretation upon history that is capable of endless exploration, and may well change the whole outlook of mankind as to the origin, significance and destiny of the human race. In particular they completely deny and—in the possibility of direct supersensible experience—can completely refute the materialistic, atheistic view of the history and destiny of mankind, which is proclaimed by Marxian Communism.

When we apply the principles of Spiritual Science to *Religion*, we find results no less striking than in the case of Science and History. In the first place, the discovery that the nature of man and the universe is spiritual, breaks down the barrier between Science and Religion. Not only does it challenge the materialistic findings of science, and lead scientific thought to new fields of exploration, by showing how the instrument of thinking can penetrate beyond sense-experience; it also brings within the scope of clear understanding and direct experience much of the content of religion, that hitherto could only be grasped by faith.

In the same way, the realisation that the spiritual evolution of mankind and the event of the Mystery of Golgotha are at the very heart of a right understanding of history, removes another long-standing barrier between secular and religious history. Spiritual Science recovers for us, but in far clearer and more conscious understanding, that ancient unity of knowledge in which the understanding of the spirit must be the supreme factor.

Spiritual Science also leads to a true understanding of the right relationship to one another of the great world-religions. Traditionally, the holding of any one religion as true implied a denial of the others, even to the extent of regarding them with hostility, as manifestations of evil. On the other hand, with the discovery by the West of the religions of the East, in the nineteenth century, and with the rise of Theosophy, the point of view evolved in some quarters of the essential equality of all religions, as varied manifestations of the same divine spirit. Rudolf Steiner, by his perception of spiritual evolution as a continuous process throughout the history of mankind, has shown how the content of each of the world-religions is the exact expression of the stage in the process of spirit-evolution, which mankind had then reached. In revealing this, he has brought a beauty and significance to the content of each religion, that a mere recital of its beliefs could never evoke.

At the same time, just because he was aware of this process as that of evolution, and because he could see objectively how the coming of Christ is the pivot of the whole process, fulfilling the past and working on for ever into the future, so he sees Christ as transcending and yet fulfilling the ancient religions, and he shows how in the actual historical event of the Incarnation of Christ the spiritual essence of the ancient religions was interwoven. This attitude towards the spiritual evolution of mankind is, after all, implied in the understanding that the physical world, and our own individual earthly lives, are the manifestation, in the successional time-process of the physical world, of a spiritual reality that exists eternally in a continuous time-relationship. It is what Christ meant when he spoke of the Jewish Law as abrogated in time by his coming, and thereby eternally fulfilled in its place in the spiritual evolution of man. It is a truth of great significance that needs to be borne in mind by the Christian Churches, in their search for the unity of Christendom.

We have already referred, in the application of these principles to history, to the effect of Steiner's revelation of primitive clairvoyance and the nature of the Ancient Mysteries upon our understanding of the beginnings of history and the absence of written records, and we illustrated this by reference to Moses and the book of Genesis. It applies in an even more startling way to our understanding of the Gospels, the ever-recurring critical uncertainty about which constitutes one of the greatest challenges to Christian faith. The discovery that in that age of partially reawakened spiritual clairvoyance, and under the deep spiritual effect of Christ upon his followers, the principle of clairvoyance played a far greater part than has ever yet been realised in the production of the Gospels,[1] is a discovery of the most far-reaching importance, for it accounts for and even necessitates the differences between them. Moreover, the fact that the Gospels originated in the disciples' clairvoyant recovery of the events of the three years they had spent with Jesus, makes it unnecessary to look for earlier written sources behind the written Gospels as we have them. The Kerugma, the content of the preaching of the Early Church on which so much emphasis has been laid in recent years, does not rest upon an authorised record, but on the direct clairvoyant preaching of those who had "known Christ in the flesh". This gives special significance to the opening words of the First Epistle of S. John. The Gospels would not be written—in fact it would not be considered desirable that they should be written—until the passing from earth of the disciples of Jesus. It would be for this reason that S. Mark would write his gospel based on S. Peter's preaching, immediately after his martyrdom.

Indeed, the understanding of the whole Bible is waiting for the flood of light which the teaching of Spiritual Science will shed upon it. A great beginning has been made by a commentary on these lines by Dr. Emil Bock, the leader of the

[1] cf. S. John XIV, 26.

Christian Community Church in Germany. It has yet to be published in an English translation. Rudolf Steiner once declared that the day would come, when, in the light of Spiritual Science, the whole of mankind would accord to the Bible the first place in the literature of the world, as the unique revelation of the nature and spiritual destiny of man.

Nor is it only the Bible that is illuminated. In its direct perception of the realities of the spirit-world and their relation to sense-phenomena, Spiritual Science sheds light upon the factual spiritual understanding of the mysteries of Christian faith and worship, such as the Incarnation, the Atonement, the Resurrection and the Sacraments.[1] Especially is this so in regard to the fundamental revelation of Spiritual Science about the nature of Man himself. The revelation of the fact of reincarnation, of man's being as involved in a continuous process of alternate physical and spiritual existence, linking him with the whole course of human evolution and human history, gives a deeper understanding of man's spiritual needs and eternal destiny.

Spiritual Science also sheds new light upon the meaning of sin, and especially "original sin", upon the absolute necessity for man of divine salvation, upon every stage of Christ's redeeming work, and especially upon the full significance of his resurrection, In particular, it gives an explanation of that strange mystery, the resurrection of the body.

In none of these directions is the revelation of religion denied or diminished. In every way it is deepened and widened, and related more clearly to every other aspect of human life and knowledge.

There is another universal sphere of human activity upon which Spiritual Science sheds perhaps the most unexpected light, and that is *Art*. There is no human activity upon which so many subjective and inconclusive opinions are held, and no time when those opinions were more diverse than they have been during this twentieth century. While there has been great variety of experiment in regard to the forms in which Art expresses itself, there is increasing uncertainty in regard

[1] See Chapter XI.

to the nature, or even the necessity, of its content. There is an ever-increasing interest in Art of all kinds, but there is, generally speaking, a complete unawareness of its intrinsic relationship to man's earthly or spiritual destiny.

It will be remembered that it was in regard to Schiller's theory of aesthetics, that Steiner first conceived the idea that the path to knowledge of the spirit-world might be found in the attainment of another level of consciousness.[1] Out of his own fully-developed spiritual knowledge he later unfolded a quite new understanding of the intrinsic relationship of all forms of Art to man's spiritual evolution.[2] "Art," he declares, "is the instrument by means of which the gods can speak to us." He relates each of the arts to the component elements in the total evolution of man's being, Architecture to the Physical-body, Sculpture to the Etheric-body, Painting to the Astral-body, Music to the Ego, Poetry to the Spirit-self, Eurhythmy to the Life-spirit.[3] In each case the art in human life is the expression of the penetration of the level of its origin into the level beneath it. Moreover, he shows that Architecture and Sculpture arose out of human memory of a spirit-existence before birth, Painting out of the experience of the spirit-world in which man finds himself in his earthly life when asleep, while Music and Poetry are an anticipation of the life that is to follow death. He treats the arts with a spiritual objectivity which, if hard at first to understand, is provocative of a quite new attitude towards them. There is nothing of which mankind stands in greater need than the recovery of the deep significance of man's artistic activities to his conscious living, but with a fuller understanding than was ever possible before.

These same facts about the nature of man cannot fail to have the greatest effect also upon one of the newest and most popularly-exploited sciences, *Psychology*. The scientific discovery of unquestionable, but hitherto unperceived, psychic phenomena in man's being and experience occurred in the

[1] See p. 39.

[2] See a series of lectures entitled *Art in the Light of Mystery Wisdom.*

[3] These are two future stages in the spiritual evolution of mankind.

last quarter of the nineteenth century, at the very time when science was becoming convinced of a materialistic interpretation of the nature and origin of man and the universe. This made it inevitable that psychic phenomena should be interpreted as arising out of, and conditioned and controlled by, man's earthly being, physical heredity, and temporal experience; and that his ideal psychological make-up should be conceived as that which would best minister to his individual and social well-being in his immediate physical existence.

The revelation, in Anthroposophy, of the eternal nature of the individual in a continuous-time existence, sheds entirely new light upon the nature of the Unconscious and of the ideal psychic content of man's being. The discovery that the psychic elements in his being have a separate and pre-existent entity to that of his material nature, and that, though conditioned in their material manifestation by the well-being or otherwise of the material body, they themselves played a creative part in its development, and continually sustain it by the balance of their working with and in it—all this opens up new fields in discovery and application for psychology and psychiatry.

Lastly, in the sphere of *Ethics*, Spiritual Science reveals a truth that is not conceived of by modern thought, and yet is of profound significance both to the understanding of life and to the ordering of human behaviour. In an age of increasing moral relativity, and of the questioning of all moral standards, it reveals that the world of ultimate reality is a world of beings, and that this realm of being is governed by moral law, working with the same certainty and inevitability as the physical laws manifest in the world of matter. The working out of these moral laws is an inevitable happening in the life of each individual, their consequences reach from life to life, and are implicit in the events of human history. While to man's earthly consciousness moral law may be a matter of opinion or belief, in the realm of spirit it is a matter of direct perception and inevitable experience. The importance of this fact can best be expressed in words used some years ago by Dr. J. H. Oldham, in the *Christian News Letter*.

> If men's minds [he wrote], were seized with the conviction that there is a natural and moral order in the universe which they can disregard only at the cost of unending frustration and suffering, there would take place a revolution in Western civilisation more fundamental than those of Communism and National Socialism.

In these important spheres of knowledge then, Science, History, Religion, Art, Psychology, and Ethics, Spiritual Science sheds new light upon the conclusions of modern thought, and, in doing so, it deepens and unifies them. It thereby establishes a claim to the serious and unprejudiced consideration of all thoughtful people, and especially of those who are the leaders of thought.

CHAPTER XV

SPIRITUAL SCIENCE AND THE CHRISTIAN CHURCHES

THE facts which we have set out so far in regard to the attitude of Spiritual Science to Christianity must present a good many problems to the minds of professing Christian people, and especially to those who are leaders or official ministers of the Christian Churches.

The simple-minded, devout Christian may wonder how he can ever penetrate to the understanding of the facts revealed by Spiritual Science and whether there is an implication that his simple faith is not enough. Again and again in his writings Steiner declares that he will never willingly disturb such a simple, living faith, which is for all people a right attitude to Christianity, an attitude through which Christ has worked through the centuries of Christendom. In a lecture on "Spiritual Science and Christianity" he quotes, as the starting-point of his theme, this saying of Hegel's:

> The deepest thought is bound up with the figure of Christ, and the greatness of the Christian religion lies in the fact that it can be understood at every stage of culture, and yet calls to the highest wisdom.

At the same time, Steiner does not present Anthroposophy only to the intellectual or subtle-minded. The deepest apprehension of it does not depend upon brilliance of intellect, but upon the right qualities of soul, and especially upon that childlike spirit which Christ declares is the key to the kingdom of heaven. Moreover, although a Christian of simple faith may not himself explore the paths of Higher Knowledge, its fruits, in the illumination and conviction which it brings to his belief, will be of inestimable blessing to him.

The thoughtful, intelligent Christian cannot fail to be deeply impressed by the Christo-centric nature of the Anthroposophical view of men and the universe, by its factual explanation of spiritual realities and theological dogmas, by the new light and understanding it brings to the study of the Bible, and by its overcoming of the barrier between sacred and secular knowledge. At the same time he will be brought up against new and startling facts, that lead him beyond the range of normal experience, and demand a restatement of some theological or traditional points of view. Nor is it only the thoughtful, orthodox Christian that will be tempted to oppose so radical a "change of mind", but opposition will come from the advanced Biblical critics, whose brilliant destructive criticism is not only disputed in its findings by Anthroposophy, but even in its methods and fundamental assumptions.

But whether the opposition is based upon sincere doubt, or whether the meeting of anthroposophical ideas with scepticism or derision is really a line of self-defence against something which threatens one's own position of intellectual superiority —the answer is the same. It is impossible to understand— still less to judge—the findings of Anthroposophy, just as much in matters of religion as in the fields of science or history, except on the ground of the fundamental concepts about man and the universe which Anthroposophy claims are revealed by "higher knowledge", and on which its findings are based. It is quite possible to reject those fundamental concepts, in which case the findings dependent upon them would fall to the ground. But to attribute a meaning to the findings, based upon another set of concepts, is a false line of criticism.

For example, Steiner's declaration that the physical and spiritual union of the divine Christ with Jesus of Nazareth took place at the Baptism of Jesus by John, has been greeted in some quarters as a revival of the Adoptionist heresy, with its denial of the essential union of the divine and human natures in Jesus. This view is based on the generally-accepted assumption that a man consists entirely of that which is the product of the union of his father and mother, and is born from his mother's womb potentially complete. If Jesus was both man and God, the divine nature, it is claimed, must have been completely incarnate within him from birth.

But Anthroposophy reveals that the nature of man is very different; that in each of us an eternal spirit-self is manifesting in our physical nature, and that in the earliest physical stages of human life that eternal self is not yet operating from within, but from without the human organism. Furthermore, its working is not manifest in full ego-consciousness until the dawn of manhood, nor effective in full soul-transformation until nearly the thirtieth year. Thus Steiner sees Jesus of Nazareth as having arrived at the full unfolding of his humanity, by the working, within his very special human organism, of an eternal human self of the greatest spiritual power and wisdom. At the baptism in Jordan that great human spirit which had been reincarnated as the higher ego of Jesus of Nazareth, yielded up its perfected human organism, with its developed human ego-consciousness, to be wholly indwelt and informed by the divine being of the Christ. In Jesus Christ, we see the being of God in complete union with the perfect being of Man. In the three years of the ministry the Eternal Word is manifest in human form, in a human life, until, in the Mystery of Golgotha, the Son of God made Man achieves the redemption of the world.

It is possible to deny the conception of man's being on which Steiner's presentation of the Incarnation is based, but it is quite irrational to attribute a meaning to that presentation, which is based on quite other fundamental concepts.

There is, of course, a natural tendency for the official leaders of the Churches to regard with suspicion a movement like Anthroposophy, and in Rudolf Steiner's lifetime he met the bitterest opposition from these quarters. Official Christianity has generally been opposed to mysticism, as a menace to ecclesiastical organisation, and subversive of its accepted ways of thought and life. This opposition expressed itself in the wildest criticisms of Steiner, as a charlatan, or an Anti-Christ, accusations which any knowledge of his writings could disprove at once. Quite recently Nicolas Berdyaev, in a very hostile and personal attack on Steiner, based on attendance at a single course of his lectures, wrote:

> Not one ray of light seemed to fall on him from above. His sole purpose and aspiration was to obtain possession of all things from below, by his own titanic devices, and to break through by a passionate effort to the realm of the spirit.

Many passages in Steiner's writings could confute this. One will suffice:

> Every occultist today clearly understands that this concept of Grace must belong to his inner practice of life in a quite special degree. There is a golden saying, especially for the occult investigator, "Have patience and wait, not until the truths are grasped by you, but until they come to you." One should say to one's self, "Grace has brought me a certain number of truths. I will wait patiently until further truths stream to me."[1]

Another line of attack—only too frequent with "orthodox" theologians—is to attempt to brush away the whole subject by declaring it to be a revival of an ancient heresy, long ago disproved and condemned. Apart from being purely negative, this criticism disregards the fact that nearly every heresy was the assertion of a neglected truth, which, however, it failed properly to relate to the rest of Christian truth. Because Steiner taught the possibility of supersensible knowledge, Anthroposophy has often been condemned as a revival of the ancient Gnostic heresy. But the Gnostics were not heretics because they possessed "gnosis", the faculty of spiritual clairvoyance. Again and again Steiner pointed out what the heresy of the Gnostics was and disclaimed it, showing at the same time how difficult it was for them, at that time, to rise to the right understanding.

> Herein [he writes], lies the difference between the Gnosis

[1] *From Jesus to Christ*, pp. 59 and 60.

and true esoteric Christianity. The Gnostics did indeed recognise Christ in his divinity. But they were never able to rise to the perception that the Word became flesh and dwelt among us.[1]

On the other hand, he himself declared that

Christ in the soul of man, Jesus of Nazareth, experienced birth and death. This means that, for the first time, a God passed through human death.[2]

The linking up of Christianity by Steiner to the ancient Mysteries is another ground of criticism of Anthroposophy by theologians. But thirty years ago the late Bishop Gore wrote:

The atmosphere of the mystery religions and of Hellenistic theosophy, with its yearning for divine fellowship and spiritual light and knowledge and salvation and a new birth, and its love of sacramental symbolism and fellowship, has a good deal to do with the diffusion of the Christian Church.[3]

Again, in his book *Liturgy and Society*, Father Hebert quotes Archbishop Söderblom as follows:

A day is coming when the science of religions will have learnt to interpret the much wider continuity of our Saviour's death and resurrection with the ancient pagan rituals.[4]

Hebert also writes himself:

The Apostles Creed corresponds to the pagan myths of the Saviour-gods. It repeats the age-long theme of the dying god. But the startling words in it are the words,

[1] Lecture on *Spiritual Science, Christianity and the Future of Mankind.*

[2] Cycle of Lectures *From Jesus to Christ*, p. 60.

[3] *Belief in Christ*, Charles Gore, p. 135.

[4] *Liturgy and Society*, A. G. Hebert, p. 56.

"suffered under Pontius Pilate." This salvation myth was enacted in the full light of history. This Saviour-God really died and rose again.[1]

The whole theme of Steiner's book, *Christianity as Mystical Fact*, is that in Jesus Christ the hidden ritual of the ancient Mysteries was openly enacted, in an actual historical life.

But in regard to the relation between Anthroposophy and the Christian Churches, we may let Steiner speak for himself. In a lecture on "Spiritual Science and Christianity" he used these words:

> It would be a misunderstanding to suppose that Spiritual Science is in any sense a new religion, or that it has any intention of setting up a new religious faith in place of the old one. To avoid all misconceptions, we may even say, when once they rightly understand it, people will realise that Anthroposophy as such, while it is the firmest and most sure support for religious life, itself is no religion. But it can nevertheless be an instrument to explain and to unfold the deepest truths and wisdom teachings, the most solemn and living mysteries of the religions. The farther we go in penetrating towards the spiritual worlds, the deeper content shall we find in the great Christian documents. The Christian documents appear to us in higher radiance, in deeper content and fulness of truth, when we approach them with that keen spiritual vision that can be gained by the help of Anthroposophy. It is true that the simplest mind can *feel* what truths there are in Christianity. But man's consciousness will not always be satisfied with a dim feeling; he will want to evolve to a higher stage, he will want to *know* and to gain knowledge. And even when his consciousness has risen to the highest heights of wisdom, there will still be deep mysteries in Christianity. Christianity is for the simplest human soul, and it is for the most highly-developed intellectuality.

[1] *ibid.*, p. 48.

Steiner himself defined Anthroposophy as follows: "Anthroposophy is a path of knowledge, to guide the Spiritual in the human being to the Spiritual in the universe." Anthroposophy deals directly, through higher knowledge, with the spiritual phenomena which are the subject matter of religion. It is not itself concerned with forms of worship or belief, or with matters of faith or order, or with the possession of a ministry or of sacraments. It arrives at direct knowledge about spiritual reality, and thereby throws light on a great deal which is the content of religion. But these facts are put forward as matters of scientific observation, and are in no sense dogmas which have to be believed if one wishes to be an Anthroposophist. While, therefore, Anthroposophy can be a great help to the understanding of the subject matter of religion, it can be approached from the standpoint of any or of no religion.

It is true that a Christian Church has come into being as the result of the teaching of Anthroposophy. This Church is called "The Christian Community". It came into being in the early twenties of this century in Germany, amongst a group of men and women who felt the need for a revival of religious life, but had not been able to find what they sought at their Universities. They had been deeply moved by the teaching of Anthroposophy, and they came to Rudolf Steiner and asked him whether he could help them to express Christian faith and worship in terms of the knowledge arrived at through Spiritual Science, in a way which would lead to spiritual renewal. Steiner at first hoped that it might have been possible to implant the new impulse for Christianity, which he saw was essential, within the existing Church organisation, but he became convinced that that was impossible, and he gave them the fullest help, out of his own initiate knowledge, in the founding of "The Christian Community". But "The Christian Community" is not part of the Anthroposophical Society. It is an independent religious body with its own organisation[1].

[1] The wording of this paragraph in the first edition quite unintentionally conveyed the impression that Dr. Steiner gave his help unwillingly. This was not so, and accordingly the paragraph has been rewritten.

It does not come within the scope of this book to give any detailed account of the Christian Community. It is a Church based on the historic fact of Christ, and its worship is centred round the Eucharist. There is much in its liturgical practice and in its interpretation of the Bible and of Christian doctrine, that will enrich the life and thought of the Christian Church generally. One of its main principles is that it does not proselytise. It does not seek to draw to itself those who are already members of other Churches, but only those who are attached to no Church or who cannot find satisfaction in their own religion. It is fairly widely spread in Germany and there are a number of centres of the Church in this country.

But while there are many Anthroposophists who are members of the "Christian Community", there are also many who belong to other Churches, and who regard their membership in their own Church as of supreme value. They have discovered that what Spiritual Science has revealed to them only strengthens and confirms their Christian faith, although at times it may lead to a re-statement or even a complete revision of the mode of expressing some Christian truths. But no conflict of loyalties is involved in being a member of any Church and at the same time a student of Anthroposophy. For Anthroposophy is not a religion, but a science.

Finally there is the traditional opposition of the Christian Church to any form of occultism, regarding it as something that is forbidden in Scripture. In the first place it is necessary to understand the background against which this scriptural prohibition came into being. We have seen how the progressive loss of true clairvoyance meant that men could only make direct contact with the spiritual world at a low and often sub-human level. Steiner himself points out how the Hebrew people was chosen for the very purpose of resisting this inevitable downward trend. They were to be a people who were to become aware of God by an inward intuition, by an almost physical awareness, and who were thus directly opposed to occultism, particularly in the debased forms in which it existed around them. It was therefore forbidden in Jewish law.

Today, however, we are facing a quite different situation. Modern science presents a world view from which any supersensible reality is excluded. On the other hand, there has awakened in the minds of very many people in the last half-century, a desire for spiritual knowledge, which is leading them into ways which, while they are not always reprehensible, are methods which will never arrive at exact spiritual fact, and can easily lead to entirely mistaken concepts. Furthermore, unhealthy and even evil forms of occultism are far more widespread than the Christian or ordinary citizen imagines.

The path which is offered by Spiritual Science is that of direct, clear, conscious spiritual knowledge, evolved by an intensification of true scientific thinking, prepared for by a real moral preparation, and leading, not to a materialised vision of spiritual reality, but to the development of the higher organs of the human organism, by means of which spirit-reality can be perceived and understood in its own proper environment. To reject Spiritual Science is to leave uncontrolled the evil occult movements of our day, and to refuse the enlightenment and certainty which is offered to religion. In these days when men's minds are absorbed in their scientific achievements, it is more than ever important to be able to read the spiritual signs of the times.

CHAPTER XVI

APPLIED SPIRITUAL SCIENCE

I. Education—Curative Education

ANTHROPOSOPHY is essentially not a mere world-concept to be argued about. It is a Movement seeking to penetrate with spirit understanding the whole of human thought and activity. As Rudolf Steiner expresses it in one of his lectures, "Anthroposophy wishes knowledge everywhere to flow into life, to give knowledge in a form which can help, wherever help is needed in the affairs of life." It will be remembered that Steiner's purpose in building the Goetheanum was that it should be a laboratory and workshop of spiritual knowledge reaching out into every department of human activity. These practical expressions of Anthroposophy have widely expanded in recent years, both in this country and in Europe; indeed, many people's knowledge of Anthroposophy is entirely limited to its expression in such activities, educational, therapeutic or agricultural.

Now, however attractive and convincing these activities may be, they will never lead to a true understanding of Anthroposophy itself, unless the central spiritual principles underlying them are understood. On many occasions Rudolf Steiner stressed this fact. It is for this reason that in this general introduction to his work we have concentrated on the fundamental principles of Anthroposophy. In any case, it would be quite impossible in such a book as this to go, at any length, into all its practical activities. Books are available on each one of them, written by those who have first-hand knowledge of the work. All that we propose to do here is to refer to some of them, indicating the elements in the world-outlook of Anthroposophy that are their guiding principles.

1. EDUCATION

There is no human activity to which the discoveries and

revelations of Anthroposophy are a greater challenge than they are to education. Anthroposophy claims no monopoly in its educational methods. It readily recognises the continuous advance that has been made in the science of teaching, and the understanding of children. Nevertheless the knowledge arrived at in Anthroposophy, that each child is an individual and eternal spiritual being, whose present earthly life has been conditioned by previous existences and has supreme importance for it in its evolution as an eternal being, creates a profound responsibility towards the child in the mind of its teacher. For the Anthroposophical teacher, the aim of education must primarily be to help the child so to adjust itself to the spiritual and material facts of its being and of its earthly existence, as to make the richest use of them.

Spiritual Science, however, does not only speak of the spirit behind and outside the physical, but of the physical itself as the expression of the spiritual. In this way it has brought a new and deep understanding of the nature and working of the physical being of man. In no department of human life is this of more importance than it is in education. Everyone is aware of the three principles at work in himself, the principles of thinking, feeling and willing. These activities function in varying but closely inter-related ways. Thinking is the activity in which we are most conscious; the essence of thinking is clear consciousness. In feeling we are less conscious. We are aware of our feelings, but we do not expect them to be capable of clear analysis and explanation. In our willing we are almost completely unconscious. That is not to say that we do not know what we are doing, but that in the act of willing itself we are unconscious, that is, in the actual process that lies between the idea of some particular action and its immediate translation into activity.

Now one of the most important discoveries that Rudolf Steiner made was in regard to the three-fold physical basis of these three activities. The idea of this came to him in his early twenties, but it was not until after thirty years of thought and meditation that he made public his discovery. While each one of these three activities of thinking, feeling and willing permeates the whole body, they are specially *centred* in three different parts of the body. The head, with the sense organs and the nervous system, is the centre of thinking. The limbs, with the processes of digestion and metabolism, are the centre of the activity of will. Between them, the chest system, with the principles of the circulation of the blood and the intake and outflow of the breath, is the seat of feeling.

This "upper man", "lower man", and "middle man" are related in a striking polarity. The quality of the "upper man", the seat of thinking, is that of *rest*. When we think, we keep still; in deep thinking we have the whole body completely at rest. The head is carried on the articulated spinal column, and the brain is cushioned in the cerebral fluid, so as to protect them, as far as possible, from the shock of the movements of the physical body in its relation to the earth.

The quality of the "lower man", on the other hand, is that of *activity*, and this is expressed in the ceaseless activity of the limbs and the metabolic processes. Every act of will expresses itself in some form of physical movement. The quality of the "middle man" lies between that of the "rest" of thinking and the "activity" of willing—in *rhythm*. The processes of breathing and of the circulation of the blood partake of an activity which is also rest, a movement in rhythm, which never ceases during the whole of life, but which, unlike the activity of the limbs, does not bring exhaustion. Feeling expresses itself in the quickening of the breath or of the heart-beat, and in the flow of blood in flushing or pallor.

Modern education tends to concentrate on the training of thinking. The reason for this is the belief, which has dominated man in the last two hundred years, that the full training of the intellect would of itself lead to right feeling and willing. That this has been proved wrong is manifest in what is constantly being said of our age, that its powers of thinking have outstripped its moral powers, and this unbalanced development is only too frequently seen in individuals. Over and over again Steiner declared that the greatest need of our age was the understanding and conscious control of the will—

and that this would only be achieved by a Spiritual Science which would lift man's thinking to a higher level, at which it would co-operate consciously with the powers of feeling and willing.

Now the reason why modern education has made the mistake of imagining that the solution of the problem lay wholly in the highest development of intellectual thinking, is that it regards the brain, the physical organ of thinking, as also the physical basis for feeling and willing. In this assumption it confused the consciousness that must accompany both feeling and willing, with the quite other physical bases of those two activities. Rudolf Steiner, on the other hand, perceiving the separate physical basis of each of these activities, and their relationship to one another, evolved an educational system in which all three could be harmoniously developed.

The clue to this he found in the physical being of the child. In the new-born infant it is obvious at a glance that the head, especially the dome-shaped upper part of the head, is far more developed than the limbs and the body, which appear almost as appendages to the head. Even the breathing and pulse in the infant have not that rhythmical regularity that later is their fundamental quality. Yet the head itself is not yet developed as the physical basis of thought. That is reserved for a much later stage. Meanwhile it has an essential function to perform. The Spiritual Scientist has learnt in "Imagination" that the forces, which function in the adult as conscious thought, first functioned—and all through life continue to function—as the "*formative forces*" which give form and shape to the physical being. From infancy these formative forces are at work, in the first seven years shaping the physical organ of the head, in the next seven years that of the rhythmical activity of lung and heart, and in the third seven years, that of the limbs and the metabolic and reproductive processes.

Side by side with this process of physical development there is a process of soul-awareness that runs in a polarically opposite direction. For the first seven years of its life the child is aware—or "awake"—only in its limbs. It discovers, it thinks, it expresses itself, it lives, in its limb activity. In doing this its functions in its *Willing*, and that all the more strongly because it is unconscious. It builds up its experience by a continuous imitation in action of its external environment.

In the next seven years the child lives in its first dawning self-consciousness, in an awareness of the rhythmical element of its being. The physical rhythmical processes of breathing and blood-circulation become perfected and the formative forces, released by the completion of its physical head-development, transform its first factual imitativeness of its environment into the processes of rhythmical, instinctive thinking and memory. It lives in its *Feeling*, in the rhythmical swinging of its limbs, in the joy of repetitive activities, like skipping, in the almost irresistible impulse to walk on the cracks or in the spaces of the pavement; in rhythmical music and singing, in the imaginative rhythm of joy and sorrow, security and fear; in the implicit belief that every question has an answer, which produces its natural trust in and respect for those who give the answers. This age of childhood is instinctively happy, because its dawning consciousness is in entire unison with its physical development.

Finally, at fourteen, the child enters the stage when it becomes conscious in its *Thinking*, in the inward process of its thought-life, in the logical thought-relationships that are independent of rhythm, and even of physical expression. It is the age of the dawning of the sense of individual being and of the power of original thinking. It tends to replace reverence and respect for authority by challenging criticism or by a shy withdrawal into the reserve of its own being. This internal revolution is accompanied by the intense physical experience of the development of the limbs to their adult perfection and the awakening of the powers and instincts of reproduction.

It is on these two polaric streams of physical and conscious development in the child, that the educational methods of a Rudolf Steiner School are based.

In the first seven years there is no attempt to give teaching of a purely intellectual kind, or that demands any element of abstract thinking. The knowledge that, even in the adult, the exercise of mental consciousness inhibits the growth-activity of the formative forces and produces a physical exhaustion that has to be repaired each night in sleep, makes it imperative that nothing shall impede the working of the formative forces in those early years, during which is built up the whole foundation of the future physical and mental life. The one aim of the teacher is to provide a daily pattern which, by the child's instinct of imitation, can lay a permanently sound foundation for the vigorous, though unconscious, activity of its will. The education of the Nursery Class depends most of all upon the teacher's education of himself or herself, as a worthy object of imitation by the children.

The next stage of childhood needs a more conscious and deliberate teaching, in order to meet the awakening powers of independent thought and memory. The dawning thought is not yet abstract. It is suffused with *feeling*, with that inner consciousness of rhythm of which we have already spoken. It thinks in pictures, that arise of themselves and awaken emotions. The understanding of this birth of thinking in the child, gives us an understanding of the dawn of thinking in the human race, that is so often misinterpreted as though it were the abstract logical thinking of the modern age. It too was a thinking in self-arising pictures that evoked emotion, and expressed themselves in myth and fairy-story.

The keynote of education at this stage is that it must be artistic, conveying a sense of rhythm and beauty. It will lead to a direct experience of music and art and, in the teaching of legend and fairy-story, it will awaken the rhythm of mood, in reverence and pity, joy and sorrow. The beginnings of scientific knowledge will be laid in an artistic understanding of Nature, in the varying pattern of her forces and in her integral relation to the child himself. Even the beginning of abstract teaching must be given pictorially and artistically. Geometry can be taught, not only objectively, but in such a way as to lead the child into an understanding of the beauty of the relationship of curves and lines and angles in the visible world. Moreover, the instinct of this age of childhood, to expect the rhythm of question and answer in the discovery of knowledge to be found in its own relationship to a trusted adult, is met by the child having the same class-teacher during the whole of the period from 8 to 14.[1]

This middle age in the child's life is perhaps the most important, in that it creates the possibility of impregnating its future thinking with feeling and will. For the teacher it is most exacting, not only in the constant necessity for artistic creativity in all his teaching, but for meeting the child's need, not now for an external model of behaviour, but for a person, in whose wisdom, honesty and love he can put his trust. But it is also for the teacher a most rich experience. For he must learn to think like a child, to suffuse the dry content of intellectual thought with feeling and will, which is the first step towards that higher knowledge which is the aim of Spiritual Science.

With the third stage of childhood, adolescence, a new educational approach is necessary. The awakening consciousness of the reality of abstract thought and logical relationship brings to the boy or girl a consciousness of the right and necessity for its mind of individual judgment. These birth-pangs of the ego cannot be avoided. This new age of adolescence is met by the withdrawal of teacher-control, in the ending of the class-teacher period. Subjects are taught by specialist teachers and, in the teaching, independence of thought and judgment are encouraged. Moreover, for the boy or girl there is brought to this new awakening to *thinking*, their own already-trained life of feeling, in which the simpler thought-realities have been already embedded. Their specialist teachers, too, are not pedants in one line of knowledge only, but the teaching of all of them is given against a background of spirit-understanding, and is suffused to its highest level with the harmony of feeling and will. At this stage of awakening independence, the necessity for this harmony can be openly imparted to the children.

All this makes adolescence primarily a conscious experience of a new level of thought and feeling, carrying with it a right to independent judgment and individual creativity. It will be an exciting discovery, in which the boys and girls, who

[1] Some subjects, of course, are taught to the child by other teachers.

have been educated together, make and share their complementary contribution. This establishes a relationship of mind and spirit between them, which keeps the burgeoning forces of growth and reproduction at their proper, less-conscious level, guided by those basic instincts of will which were unconsciously imparted in their earliest years.

Contrast this with what is so often the result of modern intellectual education. Even in the child's earliest years intellectual teaching is begun, oblivious of results to health of mind and body that may not be apparent for years. In childhood, abstract intellectual teaching cannot be delayed, for at eleven the child must pass the intellectual test which will decide its whole educational future. There is no training in feeling nor, except in a scripture lesson, in the background of spirit. For such intellectual education, adolescence only marks more intense specialisation, and the development of a purely intellectual, and generally negative, critical faculty. No wonder that the great discovery of adolescence is the upsurge of the sex-instincts. For many it is the first wave of genuine emotion that has awoken in their life, and they have no basis of the training of feeling, on which to cope with it. All they know is that, in current literature, and on the cinema screen, it appears to be, for most adults, the fullest measure of their emotional experience all their life. It becomes for the adolescent a far too absorbing experience, which can be neither controlled nor guided by an intellectual, materialistic explanation of it, which takes no account of its true spiritually-emotional side.

There is one other aspect of the educational system based on Spiritual Science that must be referred to, and that is in regard to "Temperament". The matter of "temperaments", which was taken seriously in the Middle Ages, is largely disregarded by modern psychology. No special attention is paid to the temperamental quality of a child unless it is very exaggerated, when an attempt may be made to check or to correct it. Now Spiritual Science reveals that the temperament is very closely bound up with the spiritual individuality of a person. Each human being brings into the world the karmic characteristics of his own spiritual and moral past, which unite with that which is received from the parents by heredity. In each person there are the four elements of his being, the ego, and the astral, etheric and physical bodies, and the balance of these four elements is affected by the individual's adjustment to his heredity. There are four main "temperaments", the choleric, the sanguine, the phlegmatic and the melancholic. None of them is found exclusively in any one person, but as a rule one of them, by its predominance, clearly indicates the essential nature of each of us. The choleric temperament is one in which the ego is dominant, the sanguine expresses the conscious, ever-changing interest of the astral nature, the phlegmatic, the contented well-being and indifference of a strong etheric body, and the melancholic, the difficulty of the adjustment of the spirit to a too heavy physical nature. In every individual the positive qualities of his temperament are a source of strength to him, but their exaggeration may easily rob him of the true balance of his being. A great deal of the increasing mental instability of our day is due to the failure to understand and so to take seriously this matter of "temperament".

No one but the individual himself can correct or restrain his temperament. It is the task of education to help him to do this. This is achieved in two ways. In the first place it is realised that it is both dangerous and hopeless to attempt to eradicate or correct temperament. A child *can* only act according to his temperament. It is the task of the teacher to direct the child's temperament, in its proper full activity, into the right direction. This will lead it, even in childhood, to such awareness of others as will correct its tendency to exaggeration.

Secondly, the teacher groups his whole class of children according to temperament, and plays upon it as upon an educational orchestra. He expects and produces the needed response where it can naturally be looked for, and so makes every part aware of the significance of their own self-expression and also of other forms of self-expression of which they themselves would not be capable. It is an artistic and creative method of education.

There are many aspects and applications of the educational system based upon Spiritual Science upon which we have not touched, but we have dwelt at some length upon its underlying principles. For there can be no activity more germane to Spiritual Science than the training of the individual in the art of living.[1]

II. CURATIVE EDUCATION

We have seen that the general lines of the educational system based on Spiritual Science follow the normal pattern of child-evolution, in the growing together of the individual qualities of the reincarnating human being with that which it has received by heredity through its parents. We have also seen that this regular pattern is varied in the "temperament" of each child, which, in a way, constitutes its earthly personality, and demands individual treatment.

What we have here called "individuality" can, from another point of view, equally well be called "lack of balance", for each temperament reveals that a particular one of the elements which constitute man as a physical organism, is functioning in an exaggerated or "unbalanced" way. While accepting the fact that the child can only act in accordance with its temperament, the aim of its education is that in adult life it may be able consciously to restore a measure of balance to its being.

Now a lack of balance can easily become so exaggerated as to produce abnormality, a totally unbalanced condition. A serious exaggeration of any one of the four temperaments would produce a recognisable psychopathic condition. It is well known that our generation has seen a great increase in the number of psychopathic cases, particularly in the more intellectually developed nations. Twenty years ago Alexis Carrel wrote, "In certain States (of the U.S.A.) the multitude of the insane confined in the asylums exceeds that of the patients kept in all other hospitals."[2] A century ago there were only a few cases of "Mongol" children. Today there

[1] Books on Education by Rudolf Steiner: *The Education of the Child*, *Education*, *Essentials of Education*, *Practical Course for Teachers*. See also *The Way of a Child*, by A. C. Harwood. (Anthroposophical Publishing Co.)

[2] *Man the Unknown*, by Alexis Carrel, p. 31.

are thousands and the number is increasing. In Great Britain itself the increase in the number of mentally abnormal children is becoming serious. There is a long waiting list at almost all institutions, public or private, for the care of these children. To most parents and people dealing with them, it is largely a matter of making life as tolerable as possible for them and of attempting to teach them some simple, useful occupation. To those who believe that a human being lives but once in this world, there is no more tragic sight than a mentally-defective child.

Fifty years ago Steiner declared that Western humanity was leading a completely unbalanced life, in its one-sided cult of intellect that had almost ousted any conscious attention to feeling and will, and he prophesied a great increase in mental instability in the last half of the century, unless mankind recovered its consciousness of the spiritual. Moreover, he pointed out that at that time, as a result of the spiritual evolution of humanity, many would become aware of supersensible realities, which, owing to mankind's material world-outlook, would be incomprehensible to them and would produce in them mental instability.

As a result of his spiritual understanding of man, Rudolf Steiner achieved wonderful results in the diagnosis and treatment of mentally-handicapped children. It will be remembered how, in his early years in Vienna, he was given the care of a boy who was so mentally handicapped that it seemed impossible that he could be educated at all. By establishing a direct and intimate relationship between his own soul and the sick soul of the boy, Steiner effected a complete cure. That was the beginning of his intense interest in a science of education that was based on the understanding of man as a spirit.

His approach to the mentally-handicapped child was based on the same spiritual facts that directed his general educational methods, namely, the knowledge of reincarnation and the karmic moral consequences passing from one earthly existence to the next, and the understanding of the process of human birth, as the union of the ego and its astral, etheric and physical bodies, conditioned by these karmic consequences, with the elements of substance and disposition derived from the earthly parents. Whereas in the "temperament" of a normal child there was evidence of one element in the organism dominating the others, "mental abnormality" was due to a complete failure to incarnate properly. The physical cause of this failure might be due to an accident to the physical brain, or to an inherited defect of the body, but in relation to the individual being it was in most cases to be traced further back to a karmic cause.

For example, it might be that in his previous life this now handicapped child had been dominated by a one-sided intellectualism, and that this necessitated that his next existence should be divorced from intellect, and left to the less conscious forces of feeling and will. Or again, it might have been so sunk in earthly forces, that in this life it needed to be divorced from those forces and yet lack the guiding power of a clear intellect, so that it had to live by the development of its unconscious soul-forces. Although the individual in its pre-birth spirit existence itself accepted these karmic elements in its coming life, yet, Steiner declared, it sometimes shrank away at the last moment, thus achieving that incompleteness of incarnation manifest in its abnormality. Again, it might have been karmically led to that earthly line of descent in which the inherited physical conditions of abnormality were present.

With regard to the questions so often on the lips of parents, as to why this tragedy should have been laid upon *them*, they must realise that deeper causes are present than those of chance or soulless fate. There may have been karmic relations of other kinds between themselves and their present child; or the parents themselves may have needed this burden of responsibility; or, perhaps, on account of their own achieved qualities of love and self-sacrifice, they have been chosen to guide their child's soul on its encumbered path.

If the earthly tragedy of the mentally-handicapped can be lifted out of the meaningless, accidental, irrevocable, hopeless, futureless explanations of a materialistic outlook, into the spiritual significance of a higher wisdom, in which the last word is not spoken in one earthly life and where the hidden working of a divine love and purpose is a challenge to our earthly love and service, then a new light and understanding falls upon it.

Steiner, however, did not only explain the fact of mental abnormality; he saw ways in which the handicap might be largely overcome and be converted to a spiritual fruitfulness, provided human love and devotion could rise to the necessary heights. He found a practical approach to the problem by realising how this mental abnormality expresses itself in the threefold physical polarity of head and chest and limb. Between head and limb there is incessant conflict. The consciousness of the head brings death-forces to the physical substance, while the burgeoning life-forces of the limbs dull the head's consciousness. The balance between them is kept by the middle system of the chest, the breathing and blood circulation through which the forces of head and limbs interpenetrate one another. The principle of that mediation is *Rhythm.*

One kind of mental handicap is expressed in an excess of head-forces, in a superficial, excitable talkativeness and restlessness. That must be steadied into tasks of will, but these must be artistic and rhythmic, chosen imaginatively and repeated with endless patience. Another child is handicapped with an excess of the metabolic forces of the lower man, which give him a heavily-developed body and an almost completely dull brain. He must be wakened rhythmically, by music, and emotional stories, and he must have ample space in which to give his responding physical expression.

The whole purpose of Curative Education is, not to try to evoke from the child an intellectual response of which he is, in his present condition, absolutely incapable, but by artistic creativeness to provide a rhythmic activity, which shall give controlled expression to his excessive qualities and unconsciously supplement his defects, leading him to a knowledge born out of feeling and will, in rhythmic activity.

Sometimes the device is of the simplest. The heavy-footed, earth-bound child is led to jump on his toes over a constantly-raised rope, while the earth-averse child, hardly touching the earth with his dancing feet and living apart from his companions in his own silent dreaminess, is made to jump down heavily to the ground, again and again, from a gradually raised height.

But these rhythmic devices of Curative Education do not only produce controlled consciousness and useful activities. These handicapped children can be taught to read and write, and even such abstract subjects as grammar, geography and religion.[1]

Once, late in the last war, I was in one of these Anthroposophical Homes for Curative Education, when two of H.M. Inspectors called, in order to certify to the Government that the Head of the Home was engaged in work of war-time importance. I went round the Home with them, and afterwards I found myself alone with one of the Inspectors. He volunteered to me this remark: "If we could do anything like as well in cur schools for backward children as these people do with mentally-defective children, we should be very proud of ourselves."

It is work that needs ceaseless imagination, minute observation, endless patience in constant repetition, warmth of affection and unfailing readiness of response. It is work for the most gifted and most idealistic teachers, but it brings the boundless reward of creative triumph over seemingly insuperable obstacles, and a sense of loving co-operation in a task whose end and accomplishment is beyond Time and Space. The spirit of it is summed up in two verses of a poem by A. E. (G. W. Russell):

How deep the night about that soul!
How fast the manacles! I brood
And recreate in my own heart
Its agony of solitude.

A kinsman of the cherubim
Chained in this pit's abysmal mire!
Sound for the rescue! Bugles blow!
Gird on the armoury of fire!

[1] For a fuller account of the methods of this curative work, see *Curative Education*, by Isabel Newitt (Anthroposophical Publishing Co.).

CHAPTER XVII

APPLIED SPIRITUAL SCIENCE

Healing—The State—Agriculture

III. HEALING

It has already been shown, in dealing with Curative Education, how the understanding of the being of man that reveals the principles of education passes quite naturally into the field of mental healing. An extension of this understanding and its wider application to the physical organs and functions of the body throw a flood of light on the nature of health and disease, and on the diagnosis of sicknesses and their exact remedies. By a supersensible understanding of the nature of man, and of the mineral, vegetable, and animal kingdoms amongst which he lives, the art of healing passes out of the sphere of empiricism and becomes an exact science.

In the spring of 1920 and 1921 Rudolf Steiner gave courses of lectures on Anatomy, Physiology, Pathology, and Therapeutics at the Goetheanum, to a class of over forty doctors and medical students. He would only lecture to those who were qualified or were qualifying as doctors.

The first point that Steiner established in the physiology of the human being was that man manifests continually, all through his life, the presence of two forces within his body that are polarically opposed and that need to be held in balance by a continuous process of adjustment. These are the anabolic and katabolic forces, the forces of growth and decay, the forces by which the body is built up and those by which it is destroyed, the forces of physical life and death.

Now these counteracting forces operate through the interplay of the four constituent members of man's being of which we have often spoken, the physical[1] body, the etheric body, the astral body and the ego. The etheric body is the seat of the forces of growth and is closely united with the physical body. The astral body is, in the first place, the origin of the exact form of the body and its organs, and, to this end, it controls the thrusting, building-up life-forces, of the etheric. It is also the seat of conscious feeling, and, as such, it is found in the animal world. There, it plays the most important part in beings which are more self-contained than the plant-world, having themselves to seek their food, or their mate, and to care for their young by the forces of inner instinct. The astral body in them expresses itself in a sense of well-being in their organs and their functions, and a warning sense of pain or discomfort when disorder arises. This is found also in man. The natural, healthy functioning of his organs brings a sense of well-being, and even of pleasure, as in the pleasure of eating. Disorder is expressed in pain and discomfort.

Now, as we saw in an earlier chapter, the activity of the ego and astral within the human organism expresses itself by means of the same etheric forces which build up the body, and consequently, when it is at work, the building-up forces are diminished. We saw, in the last chapter, how important it was not to interfere with this formative building-up work of the ego and astral in the early years of childhood, by drawing the ego into a too-early development of intellectual consciousness. But in addition to restricting the building-up forces, the ego-astral, in the process of ordinary consciousness, uses up and destroys the physical substance in the organism.

There is thus a double etheric-physical wastage going on during all human consciousness, the diminishing of etheric forces, and the wastage of the physical body. This is perpetually balanced in the daily rhythm of waking and sleeping.

[1] It is important to distinguish between two uses of the word "physical": (i) when, as here, it refers to the body as formed of material substances of the same kind as are to be found in Nature, and which at the death of the human being are reabsorbed into the mineral kingdom; and (ii) when it is used of the whole human organism, when it includes all the four elements expressed in it.

In sleep the ego and astral withdraw in their activity of self-consciousness from the human organism, releasing all the etheric forces for their up-building activity, and working upon the etheric-physical organism from outside in the restoration and control of form. In waking, the ego and astral return to their life of physical consciousness, in which alone man's spiritual evolution on earth can be accomplished, but which is at the same time the gradual destruction of his physical organism.

Here we should note another feature of man's being to which Rudolf Steiner directs our attention. The human organism is a spiritual-physical organism, to an extent which differentiates it from all the other phenomena of Nature. Although man lives in the midst of the three kingdoms of Nature, mineral, vegetable and animal, and although he shares in some measure the substance of these kingdoms, yet because he is essential spirit, he differs from them in the laws of his being, which cannot be interpreted by the laws which govern theirs. Each man is a little spirit kingdom in the midst of the kingdoms of Nature, isolated between the outer skin of his body and the walls of his intestinal canal. Everything that passes into his organism from Nature, has to be metabolised by its processes, in order that it may conform to the spiritual-physical laws of man's being. Everything that cannot be so metabolised is rejected in the excreta of his intestines or his other organs. If the excretion is prevented he will soon die. Even the air he breathes is metabolised. Even warmth does not affect him as it would other natural bodies, by a continual raising of his inner temperature. It too is metabolised as it penetrates him.

Let us return now to the consideration of the fundamental process of growth and destruction, integration and disintegration, that we have seen as the main principle of man's being, in the inter-working of the four elements of which he is composed. We must now relate this further to that great discovery of Steiner of man as *physically* a threefold being, each part, as we saw in considering education, being the physical base of one of his three great spiritual activities of

Thinking, Feeling and Willing; the Head (Nerves and Senses) system the basis of Thinking, the Chest (Heart and Lung) system the basis of Feeling, and the Limb and Metabolic system the basis of Willing.

When we consider Man as a physical organism we see these three physical bases functioning in the great process of integration and disintegration. The Lower or Metabolic system is the centre of the etheric building-up processes, the Upper or Head system is the centre of the working of the ego, in the ego-astral consciousness, resulting in the process of disintegration in the physical substance. Between them the Middle system of the Heart and Lung mediates, as Feeling mediates between Thinking and Will. In it the astral body is dominant, working upwards to the ego in clear consciousness and downwards to the etheric-physical in its lower consciousness and in formative control.

This does not imply that these forces and their working are restricted to these centres, but only that these constitute their respective physical bases. The building-up forces are distributed over the whole body; the sense-organs, chiefly centred in the head, are found elsewhere even to the periphery of the skin and, indeed, in every organ; while the rhythmic processes of breathing and blood-circulation extend everywhere, carrying up to the head the building-up forces of the Lower man, and bringing to the limbs and lower organs the forces of consciousness. In every organ and part of the body there are the three forces, building-up (etheric), destructive (ego-astral), balancing (astral), but in each part one function is dominant. The kidney primarily belongs to the metabolic system as an organ of excretion, but it is also a sense-organ. The heart and lungs are sense-organs, as is shown by the response of breathing and pulse to emotion; they also contribute to the building-up of the body. Their primary function, however, is rhythmic, distributing and controlling the forces of growth and consciousness.

Now health depends upon the *general* balance throughout the whole body, between these forces of physical integration and disintegration, a balance which is chiefly maintained in the daily rhythm of sleeping and being awake. Besides this, there is the particular balance in each organ, in accordance with its specific function, the due balance of sense-force and growth-force through the rhythmic forces of the bloodstream and breath.

Illness is the disturbance of this balance. It can occur in the general system or in any organ. It can arise in several ways. The etheric forces of growth may be weak through lack of nourishment or an enfeebled inherited constitution. This is generally manifested in chronic illnesses. Again the astral formative controlling forces may be too weak, which would lead to an exuberant etheric growth and a weakening of the excretory functions. Or again, the astral, not sufficiently controlled by the ego, may work too intensely into an organ and inhibit its etheric growth. Then the natural pleasure and sense of well-being in the function of the organ becomes pain. Again, the ego-astral forces of consciousness, which belong to the sense and nerve system of the head, may be over-developed and flow into the metabolic limb system. There, Steiner declared, these forces tend to form swellings or carcinomatous growths, an exercise of the same function by which these ego-astral forces originally formed out of physical substance the sense organs. These are matters for trained doctors to examine, but one cannot fail to notice that the increase in these carcinomatous diseases in our day is paralleled by the widespread development of the forces of the intellect, and their extension in consciousness into realms of bodily activity that were formerly unconscious or were controlled in rhythmic subconsciousness.

This distortion of balance in the physical organism would arise essentially out of the distortion of balance in the human soul and spirit. The powers of Thinking (Ego), having lost the sense of their true relation to the spirit, have associated themselves in purely Intellectual Thinking (Ego-Astral) with the instincts of Life and Growth (the Etheric) in the lower bodily nature of man—as centred on and satisfied by the material world—and the feeling-life arising out of that lower nature. Thus the origin of the physical unbalance called disease would be related to the human spiritual unbalance, scientific materialism.

In regard to *remedies*, Spiritual Science has a great deal to say. Apart from cures effected by altered ways of living and by diet, the remedy is best effected by some substance, either vegetable or mineral, that can restore the balance, either by checking the too-strongly acting forces or by stimulating those that are lacking. The lack of balance between the astral and etheric forces is best dealt with by plant remedies; that between the ego and the astral, by mineral remedies. Steiner deals at great length with the matter of diagnosis and remedy, but these considerations are outside the scope of this book, and in any case can only properly be appraised by medically-trained persons. But his supersensible perception enabled him to penetrate, far more deeply than by the ordinary methods of natural science, into the nature and qualities of plants and minerals, and so to apply them in a very exact way. For example, the same forces of life and growth work in the plant as in man, but are controlled by astral forces acting *from outside*. Yet Steiner reveals that in some cases these astral forces penetrate into a plant in an abnormal way. These are the so-called poisonous plants, for the astral properties in them, taken into the human system, increase dangerously the destructive, disintegrating forces within man himself. Nevertheless, properly prepared and applied, these plants can be used to supply a deficiency in astral forces.

Again, in regard to the growing forces of the plant, Steiner speaks of the necessity of special care in collecting and preparing the remedies, which at first sight may seem meticulous. It might appear to be quite unimportant as to whether a plant, needed for a remedy, was gathered in the spring or the autumn. But a year in plant-life is equivalent to a lifetime in a man. No one would expect to find the same quality of life-forces in the decay of old age as in the fresh budding of youth. So too the life-forces of the plant are different in the spring when they are shooting up to meet the down-streaming cosmic forces, and in the autumn when they are sinking back into the roots of the plant.

In Spiritual Science there is no question of following blindly one of the schools of medical thought. It is a matter of exact diagnosis, recognising the spirit background and interrelationships of the human organism. Some cases, Steiner declared, would need allopathic treatment, others homeopathic. In regard to allopathy, Steiner always expressed his admiration for its research into the nature of disease and its achievements in the realm of cure. But in its ignorance of the supersensible background of man, allopathy seeks to explain the origin of disease in the secondary phenomena, the bacteria, the ground for whose existence has been provided by the spiritual-physical lack of balance in the organism or in some particular organ. Homeopathy certainly attempts to deal with man as a whole, but it tends to make wide general claims for the efficacy of a particular remedy, because it has not the spiritual-scientific knowledge to make an exact diagnosis. "Nature-cure" practitioners rightly emphasise the importance of man's relationship to his natural environment, but, knowing nothing of the spirit background of Nature, they apply their methods in a materialistic way.

During Steiner's lifetime spirit-healing was hardly recognised, but at the present time it is being looked upon with much more favour, both by the Christian Churches and by the medical profession, and is spreading widely. Here too it is all too easy to adopt wrong methods. If all illness is regarded as an extraneous evil which can be removed by the exercise of external spiritual forces, then we begin with a wrong picture. It has to be realised that illness arises in a lack of balance, in an endless fluctuation between integration and disintegration, without which there could be neither life nor spirit-consciousness. Spirit-healing must never disregard the boundless wealth of remedies that lie in a spiritual scientific understanding of man's relationship to the other kingdoms of nature. Moreover, while faith and external spiritual power can effect certain cures, nothing except the conscious co-operation of the individual can cure disease caused by an unbalanced assertion of the ego-astral forces.

At this moment, when new and baffling diseases are springing up and endless empirical experiments are being made in scientifically-concocted chemical remedies, Spiritual Science offers a new and rational spiritual background to man's existence as a human organism, and offers a key to the understanding and application of endless remedies in the plant and mineral world. This provides a wonderful field for new discovery to scientific men with a love of healing in their hearts. There are many highly-qualified medical men in this country and in Europe who are practising Anthroposophical doctors.[1]

The key to the whole situation is the true knowledge of man given in Spiritual Science. It is of deep significance that near most of the ancient Mystery temples there was a healing-centre, and that one of the most famous mystery sects called themselves "Therapeutae" (Healers). Above all, that He, who, above all others, brought the secret and power of the spirit-world into human consciousness, manifested Himself as the Healer of men's souls and bodies.

IV. THE STATE

If Man is sick in his inner being and in his physical body he is no less sick in his communal life. The State is sick, almost unto despair. For the last seventy-five years this consciousness of disease in the State has grown, and it has provoked many suggested remedies. At the present moment the world stands in a tension of international antagonism. On the one side are the united exponents of a revolutionary social remedy; on the other, a medley of opinions, from those of somewhat less drastic cures, to those of reactionary *laissez-faire*, all of them united only in the conviction that the revolutionary remedy has increased the disease. Mankind as a whole is longing and praying for an end of "the cold war", but it can never end merely with the easing of international tension. For it is only the symptom of the social sickness, the germs of which are working visibly in every State community today.

[1] See especially *Fundamentals of Therapy*, by Rudolf Steiner and Ita Wegman, M.D. (Zurich). It was only a few days before his death that Steiner corrected the final proofs of this book.

Not until man discovers the nature of the disease that is disrupting his communal life, can he hope to heal it.

Rudolf Steiner, with his spirit-knowledge of the nature of Man and the Universe, was able to penetrate to the understanding of this State-sickness. We have already seen, in our consideration of his life, that, at the conclusion of the first world war, he saw the problem of Europe as much more a human social problem than a matter of political diplomacy, and that he propounded to the bewildered people of Germany a new social order, that for a few years aroused the greatest interest, until the vested interests opposed to it united to destroy it.

Steiner perceived that the State was sick of the same disease as that which was afflicting man's inner consciousness as a human being, and also his physical organism. The State was being regarded as a homogeneous entity, instead of as a complex threefold organism in which the parts should function in balanced interdependence. As a result, one vital function was almost disregarded, while the other two tried to usurp each other's functions, or united in an unnatural alliance, in which neither could function properly and the whole body-politic was sick.

The State, like man, is a threefold entity. In the first place there are the individual functions which each citizen contributes as a creative spirit-being. These express themselves in religion, art, inventive genius and in education. This is the body-spiritual in the State. At the other end there is the body-economic, in which, both corporately and as individuals, the community derives from the outside world its resources, and transmutes them into commodities to meet its own needs. Between them, and balancing them, is the body-politic, an independent body of the "rights" which must exist between men, both in those same free individual activities and also in the complex organism of economic life. This is the realm of legal and social enactment.

In the Middle Ages man lived in an instinctive balance of these three elements in his common life. He recognised himself in his spirit nature, and he recognised his craft as the natural expression of that nature, while the realm of "rights" controlled his social relationships and his somewhat elementary economic life. After the sixteenth century, when the practical reality of the spiritual became less certain, the social "intellect" began to function only in the realm of "rights", regarding the individual man only as a political unit. It also concerned itself increasingly, but unrelatedly, with the growing realm of "economics". With the vast scientific and industrial expansion of the nineteenth century, the "economic" realm became dominant and functioned in almost complete independence. The realm of "rights" remained as before, but the new and inhuman relationships into which the workers were drawn in the "economic" absorption of communal life, were quite unregulated. In great measure the realm of "rights" functioned to keep the realm of "economics" independent.

From this arose the social revolution. To the workers, hopelessly enmeshed in the net of economics, in which they and their labour were simply an impersonal "commodity", life had no human significance. But to them the spirit no longer meant anything. The upper and middle classes appeared to retain religion and culture as a private concern, having no inherent relation to the State or to public activity. But the worker had little opportunity for either. To him the one unquestionable reality was the economic realm which absorbed his whole existence, and he was easily persuaded that the spiritual, in all its aspects, was only an "ideology", something born of the human mind, with no reality, force, or significance of its own.

He saw, however, the realm of "rights" and the power of the vote, as a means for securing for himself a share of the fruits of industry and a due recognition of himself as, not a spiritual, but an economic entity, In the process of the revolution, power tended to accumulate in the hands of those who controlled "rights", the politicians, and just as "economics" had dominated "rights", so now the politicians claimed for themselves the control of "economics". This is fatal, for either economics wilt because they do not function under their proper laws in the hands of those who understand them, or the leaders of industry seek to control the realm of "rights". In neither case is the workers' lot improved, and the State is still diseased.

The only cure is to recognise the threefold nature of the State and to ensure that each "realm" functions independently and yet all in balanced harmony. For this, "rights" and "economics" must function separately, but, most important of all, the "spiritual" must be recovered, not as a matter of faith in some "quite other" reality, nor as a renewed interest in culture as a form of leisure-activity, but as the actual background of visible, sense-reality, and the source of its strongest impulses. As Steiner expressed it:

> In a human community where spiritual life plays a merely ideologic role, common social life lacks one of the forces that can make and keep it a living organism. What ails the body social today, is impotence of the spiritual life. And the disease is aggravated by the reluctance to acknowledge its existence.

When Steiner published *The Threefold Commonwealth* in 1919, much of his diagnosis was not apparent in fact. The Russian Revolution was still an uncertain development, the reality of the social revolution was not admitted—nor even realised—in many Western countries, and the future of Europe was still regarded as a matter of political state diplomacy.

The situation is very different now. The problems of diplomacy today are so baffling because they are not those of conventional politics, but of fundamentally-opposed sociologies, neither of which is aware of the disease from which both are suffering. Moreover, we are all beginning to realise that the sociological problem exists everywhere.

Indeed, it has become manifest and acute in a little-expected quarter, although Steiner prophesied in 1919 that it might easily arise there, and with the most serious consequences.

Steiner saw clearly the age-long opposition between East and West, the East with its instinctive belief in the spiritual, the West with its scientific materialism and economic power. World-economics were bringing them into a relationship in which the East would feel themselves—as the workers of the West had felt—enmeshed in the economic net. It might well be, he said, that they would jettison their spiritual heritage as no longer effective, and concentrate, by the power of world "rights" and of vast numbers on establishing their claim to a materialistic economic equality. The vast spirit-void sociology of Soviet Russia might well hasten that day, as it is already doing. Then mankind would indeed be destitute of its spirit-consciousness. Already that cloud on the horizon is larger than a man's hand.

The reconstruction of human society evolved in Steiner's *Threefold Commonwealth* cannot be expected to be realised in a short time. It demands the courage and vision of men who are prepared to re-think the whole problem of human society. But the first, and absolutely necessary, step is that which is offered in Spiritual Science, the direct knowledge of spirit as the objective reality in man and the universe, and the understanding of the State as a threefold organism.

In the eighteenth century man's dream of human rights expressed itself as, "Liberty, Equality, Fraternity". Steiner pointed out that it was because men sought to realise these in the State, conceived as a single homogeneous organism, that they failed. When men were equal, they were not free, and fraternity remained a remote ideal. But it will be a different matter when each is realised as the proper function of one of the three independent "realms" of the life of the State. In the realm of Spirit, liberty is the essential keynote; in the realm of "Rights", equality is a necessity, and the realm of "Economics" can only freely function in the spirit of fraternity. Only in the balanced independent functioning of the three spheres of State-activity, will that great ideal of communal human life be realised.[1]

[1] For a full statement of these principles related to our present situation, see *The Three Spheres of Society*, by Charles Waterman (Faber 1946).

V. AGRICULTURE

So far we have considered Spiritual Science in its application to man in relation to himself and to his fellow-men. But there is also another relationship of the greatest importance of which man has become almost unconscious in its spiritual significance, and that is, his relationship to the world in which he lives, the Earth and the world of plant and animal. While there is, in the hearts of most men and women, especially in this country, an instinctive love of Nature and animals, yet, from a general economic point of view, man has come to look upon the Earth and Nature as objects of exploitation for his own wealth and comfort. The farm has been treated like a factory, efficiency being estimated by the ratio of immediate production to costs and revenue. This has been accelerated in the last fifty years, one factor being the short-term demands of war for increased immediate supplies.

This policy of treating the farm as a factory, and the widely expanded use of chemical fertilisers to secure increased production, has caused apprehension in the minds of many thoughtful agriculturalists and horticulturalists. To them a warning has been sounded in soil-erosion and in the multiplication of plant and animal diseases and it has aroused a wide-spread reaction, resulting in a demand for organic manures rather than organic plus artificial manures, and for a different attitude towards the earth as a living organism. Such views have been ably expressed by Lady Eve Balfour in her book *The Living Soil* and in *The Rape of the Earth* by Jacks and Whyte, and there are other innumerable publications dealing with these pressing questions.

Now Rudolf Steiner pointed out these dangers thirty years ago and in his principles of agriculture proceeded even further. He saw the error of modern scientific agriculture, not so much in its methods as in its concepts, in its failure to understand the spiritual relation between man and nature, and to consider the influences emanating from the various extra-terrestrial bodies, in addition to the obvious influences of the sun. These cosmic forces which organise matter into living forms, and which are hidden in organic and inorganic matter, are being studied by those who are following his methods of agriculture and some results of these studies have been published.[1]

Rudolf Steiner often spoke of the spiritual relation between man and Nature in his books and lectures, and in the spring of 1924, at a great conference of farmers and landowners at the house of Count Karl Keyserlingk at Koberwitz in Silesia, he gave a course of eight lectures, which have become the foundation of a now widespread Anthroposophical agriculture.

The first principle that Steiner applied was that of which we have seen man had become unconscious, even in regard to his own being—the reality of spirit-activity in and behind the manifestations of Nature. The Earth is not a dead mineral substance in which living seed is planted, but it is a living organism, with its own life-forces, which, in the plants springing from its surface, rise up to meet the downpouring life-forces of the Cosmos. Just as in our own bodies, so in the Earth, the mineral substances are present in transmuted form, in living processes, and not as they are found in chemical analysis. In that transmuted form their potency is, not as substance, but as life-force.

This brings us to the second principle, that the primary factor in the nature of the Earth is not substance, but life, and that the aim, in replenishing the Earth, is to restore its *life-force*. This relation to life-force explains the use of the word "Bio-Dynamic", as applied to the agricultural methods based on Rudolf Steiner's teaching.

Any mineral substance put into the Earth has to be transformed into life-force, and it is obvious that it will be more effective if introduced organically. Here we arrive at one of the most important elements in biological-dynamic agriculture, the development of the compost-heap. In this the vegetable waste-products of every kind are composted in a certain way, and treated with special preparations made from plants in conjunction with animal-forces. The result is a perfect humus, restoring to the earth its necessary substance

[1] *The Etheric Formative Forces in Universe, Earth and Man* by Dr. Günther Wachsmuth.

already vitalised, and enabling the plants to open themselves up to the cosmic forces. This revitalisation of the plant can also have effect on the thinking capacity of man, assisting creative and constructive thought through enhanced nutrition. For those particular forces, named by Steiner the "etheric formative forces", which are active in plant growth, are also closely associated with the etheric body of man, which, as we have seen, plays a most important part in the activity of thinking.

Another principle that Steiner revealed about the processes of Nature is one which we have seen plays so large a part in the being of man, the principle of balance. There is a continual balance and rhythm between the forces of earth and the forces of the cosmos, in the growth of plants and in the changes of the months and of the seasons. There is also the balance between one kind of plant and another, one producing forces that mitigate the dangers threatening another. For instance, with regard to insect pests, the spiritual-scientific understanding of nature reveals that certain plants can, by their association with others, protect the latter from their insect enemies. The aim of Bio-dynamic agriculture is so to develop the characteristic vital forces of plants that they are less vulnerable to disease and to pest infestation, and where attacked are more capable of resistance. Prophylaxis is aimed at rather than the treatment of diseased conditions, although these are, of course, treated. Poisonous sprays are not used, but decoctions, made from certain plants, by special preparations, are used for spraying plants and soil against rusts, mildews and other fungoid diseases with the aim of restoring balance of forces.

In short, Steiner showed that in agriculture the farm is an organism, in which man, animal, and plant should live in a relationship to each other and to the Cosmos, that can make this organism self-supplying. In this the farmer works as an artist in the medium of Nature, as another artist works in some other medium, but to work rightly he must know and observe the laws and relationships inherent in that medium.

In all this, bio-dynamic agriculture is not indifferent to

the need of economic efficiency, but rather than employ forced development for immediate profit—which may prove an unsatisfactory policy in long-term results—it seeks to reach the highest level of harmonious growth by study of the imponderables and the dynamics of man, animal and plant, which, in right proportions, should result in a correct physical constitution. Quality is desired rather than quantity, but a quality that will produce quantity, and this development of quality is an important factor in dealing with the threatened shortage of the world-supply of food. To rely on physical analysis alone can be misleading as to nutritive values, and, as an indication of the quality of living forces present in a subject under observation, certain methods of crystallisation and capillary dynamolysis are employed.[1]

The recovery of the true relationship between man and nature is one of the greatest spiritual hungers of mankind, a hunger present in the hearts of many men and women today. It can be satisfied by a changed attitude towards universe, earth and man which, as we have seen, rests on spiritual-scientific understanding. True spiritual understanding can work with the latest machinery in the right way. The relation of Man to the Earth, on which, and by which, he lives, is almost his earliest conscious relationship. For it is that to which that great spiritual leader Zarathustra in the Old Persian civilisation directed him, that he might thrust his "golden blade" into the earth. He can recover that relationship in the light of the knowledge of his own spiritual being, and the recovery of it, with the accompanying deepening of his sense of responsibility towards the earth, will be potent in bringing his spiritual nature to its highest possibilities.

What we have here given is only a sketch of some elements of the new knowledge of agriculture imparted by Steiner, sufficient to illustrate the principles on which it is based. The Biodynamic movement is spreading widely, and there are not only many centres in which it is practised, but there are

[1] Further information on this subject can be found in the following books: *Formative Forces in Crystallization*, by Dr. E. Pfeiffer, *Capillary Dynamolysis*, by L. Kolisko and *Capillary Analysis*, by Maria Hauschka.

agricultural laboratories, testing and experimenting on these lines. Many publications are available about it. It is one of the developments of Spiritual Science that makes the widest appeal.

In these two chapters, we have shown the application of Spiritual Science in many practical directions. By themselves these activities are no substitute for knowledge of its central principles and the conscious development of one's own higher self. But in their demonstration of the applicability of these principles to so many human activities, and by the illumination which they shed upon the problems inherent in these activities, they are an encouragement to press forward on the path to higher knowledge, in the hope that it is a path which will lead mankind into the light of a new age.

CHAPTER XVIII

THE WAY FORWARD

IN bringing to a conclusion this attempt to give to our scientifically-minded age an explanatory introduction to the Anthroposophy of Rudolf Steiner, the inevitable feeling is one of the inadequacy of the achievement. Steiner's output was so vast—some forty books and over five thousand lectures and lecture-cycles, covering, not only the whole range of human experience, but the untrodden realms of the spirit—that one can only be conscious of the extent of one's omissions.

The aim of the book, however, has not been to skim the whole surface of Steiner's thought, but to penetrate as deeply as possible to the core of his teaching—the assertion of the living reality of spirit in man and the universe, its discoverability in actual experience, and its applicability to the problems before which Humanity stands bewildered. There has been no attempt to conceal any facts of the spirit, because they are startling or unfamiliar, or because they challenge widely-accepted conclusions of modern thought, but rather to consider them as dispassionately and scientifically as possible, both in themselves, and in the light they throw on human knowledge. The aim has not been to produce a series of conclusions that demand assent, but to throw enough light on the pathway to spirit-knowledge and spirit-understanding of the world, blazoned by Rudolf Steiner, as to encourage the thinkers of our day to follow up and test for themselves his conclusions.

The serious student of Anthroposophy, however, will find himself confronted, almost from the start, with difficulties which challenge his perseverance and sincerity of purpose. The first difficulty is in the nature of the subject itself. Spiritual Science reveals facts of which, in his normal consciousness, he is unaware. Moreover, this revelation is based upon the clairvoyant perception of Rudolf Steiner, the factual reality of which he cannot directly prove or disprove. His first instinct will be to inquire whether others have possessed this clairvoyant vision, and also whether Steiner's own followers have developed "higher knowledge" along the lines laid down by him.

There is, of course, no question that others besides Steiner have described many of the facts of his spiritual world-picture, which they have discovered by clairvoyance. In several of his lectures Steiner discusses the whole history of clairvoyant esoteric knowledge, leading right up to his own day. Most of the knowledge had been kept secret within esoteric circles, but in some instances, as in the writings of Madame Blavatski and others, it had been made public. In most cases, however, the clairvoyance was atavistic and was unconsciously developed. What distinguishes the clairvoyant perception of Steiner was his clearly thought-out and fully-conscious method of clairvoyant development, and the completely scientific manner in which the facts of the spiritual world, as he perceived them, were co-ordinated and related to known physical phenomena.

In regard to Steiner's followers, it is clear that none of them has developed a clairvoyant knowledge comparable with his own. At the same time, many regularly follow the path of self-development which Steiner taught and have reached varying stages in higher knowledge, at which they have verified for themselves the facts revealed up to that level.

In regard, however, to the difficulty felt about the validity of clairvoyant revelation to the non-clairvoyant, there are several points to bear in mind. In the first place, no one can have absolute certainty of the validity of "higher knowledge," except by his own direct experience of it. If any number of Steiner's followers had developed such knowledge, it would be open to the critic to say that it was all a matter of "suggestion", based on the known teaching of Anthroposophy.

Secondly, Steiner claimed no monopoly in his clairvoyance. Indeed he urged men and women to seek the higher knowledge he possessed, and he left detailed instruction on the true path to it. There is great need today that many should have the courage, determination and patience to tread that path.

Thirdly, it would be quite unscientific to expect to find any complete *material* proof of the validity of "higher knowledge" at the level of physical consciousness. That would be a contradiction in terms. It is equally unscientific to refuse to consider so important and challenging a world-concept as this, merely because it is frankly declared that it was arrived at by supersensible perception. That does not make it less credible than if it were based upon assumed hypotheses.

There are, however, two grounds of assurance in regard to clairvoyant knowledge that are available to the non-clairvoyant investigator. The first is based on the knowledge of the character of the clairvoyant and on the consideration of the manner in which he attained and expounded his clairvoyance. This we have attempted to supply in the case of Rudolf Steiner, in the biographical section of this book. The other ground of assurance is based on a study of the findings of this clairvoyance, in regard to their rational relationship to one another and to the known facts of Science. Steiner repeatedly declared that while clairvoyant perception is required for the discovery of Spiritual Science, it is not required for testing and proving it. He pointed out that it is not necessary, nor possible, for everyone to become clairvoyant, but that it is within the power of every human being to develop insight into the spiritual world, by an intelligent study of the facts revealed to clairvoyant perception. For the great majority of Anthroposophists their conviction of the truth of Spiritual Science is based on such study.

At the commencement of this study the natural reaction of our logical thinking will be to suspect these unfamiliar facts and to marshal arguments against them. On the assumptions of ordinary thinking this is not difficult to do, as every student of Anthroposophy has found for himself in the early stages of his study. It was the experience of the author of this book that, at his first reading of *The Philosophy of Spiritual Activity*, the margin of almost every page was heavily scored with logical and philosophical queries and objections. At the next reading half of them were deleted, and in subsequent reading they have almost all disappeared.

The facts that Spiritual Science reveals lie in a different level of consciousness from that in which our normal logical reasoning works, and they are related to elements in our own being of which we are unconscious. But if the facts imparted to us are not immediately rejected, if we give them unprejudiced consideration, they will awaken a response in those deeper levels of our being, and we become aware of this in the growing perception that the facts present us with a more complete and comprehensible picture of ourselves and our environment than we possessed before. This feeling, if allowed to live and deepen in us, grows into a rational understanding of the truths of Spiritual Science.

A mere hurried reading of the presentation of Rudolf Steiner's teaching, can only result—in self-defence—in a sceptical rejection of it. Only the willingness of the student to read thoughtfully, and to think over again and again, without prejudice, difficult or startling statements, and to allow them, meanwhile, to work upon his mind, will enable him to arrive at an apprehension of Anthroposophy.

Another difficulty lies in the fact that all Steiner's writings were in German, and that of a somewhat unusual and highly imaginative kind. Many of them are translated into English, but the English translations, especially the earlier ones, suffer from the fact that some of the translators were unfamiliar, either with Steiner's own German style, or with the correct English idiom, and in some cases do not appear to have fully understood the exact significance of that which they were translating. The result constitutes a real difficulty to the English student, with no knowledge of German. One of the most urgent needs of Anthroposophy is a complete revision of the early English translations. Nevertheless, we owe a great debt to those who, with their limited resources, both in men and money, made the translations we have. The latest translations are of a higher standard. Rudolf Steiner himself said that for Great Britain to grasp Anthroposophy it needed to be presented through the thought of British minds.

A third difficulty is in the nature of the original literature of Steiner's teaching. It falls into two parts, the books which he prepared for publication, and the vast number of lectures which he gave to Anthroposophical groups, on all kinds of subjects, over a period of twenty-four years. The books were most carefully prepared and revised by him with a view to general publication, and in many of them he opened his subject with an introductory exposition of the groundwork of his Anthroposophical teaching, linking it up with the current thought-concepts of his readers.

The lectures and lecture-cycles have a quite different background. They were given in response to the request of groups of Anthroposophists, who asked Steiner to speak on various subjects in the light of Spiritual Science. Steiner knew that his audience already possessed a background of knowledge of the principles of Anthroposophy, and that he assumed in his lectures. To anyone reading them without this background of Anthroposophical knowledge, the lectures would often appear incomprehensible, and even irrational, and would provoke hostile criticism which only spiritual knowledge could dispel.

Moreover, the lectures were not intended to be preserved as written records. They were not even composed in the usual manner of lectures. The knowledge given in them was the result of higher knowledge, arrived at in meditation, and they were given directly out of that knowledge, without notes. It was, of course, natural that those who heard these lectures should wish to preserve a record of the unique knowledge they gave, and so the habit arose of having them taken down at the time in shorthand. Steiner declares, in his autobiography, how averse he was to this, but how he had to bow to the inevitable human situation. It was quite impossible for him to give them a more permanent form. He declares how hopeless these shorthand reports appeared to him, and how he would have found it easier to re-write them entirely—a task quite beyond the resources of his time or strength.

For a long time these unrevised records of his lectures were allowed to be issued only to members of the Anthroposophical Society, but, with the growth of the Movement and the general desire for spiritual knowledge, this restriction was removed, though they are always issued with a note that they are based on shorthand reports unrevised by the lecturer, and can only be appraised on an understanding of the principles of Anthroposophical knowledge.

This brings us to one feature of Anthroposophy which differentiates it from other forms of occult knowledge. Secrecy has always been the rule of occultists in regard to their knowledge, on the very ground that it can only be understood by those who have been initiated into knowledge of the spirit, and that by the uninitiated it will inevitably be rejected with scorn, and hostility to those who impart it. This, of course, is the meaning of Jesus' words: "Give not that which is holy to the dogs, neither cast ye your pearls before swine, lest they trample them underfoot and turn again and rend you." On all occultists was laid the vow of secrecy.

Now when Rudolf Steiner, in the last years of the nineteenth century, came to the full development of his occult perception, he was confronted with this problem of secrecy. He was not the only one to have arrived at this knowledge, and by it he was brought into touch with others, who were bound by this rule of secrecy. So intense, however, was his awareness of the errors into which the materialism of the Natural Science of his day was leading humanity, and of the terrible evils that threatened mankind from the dark hostile forces of the spirit world itself, and the little-known, but desperately evil, forms of occultism existent in the world, that he decided that this ancient rule of secrecy must be broken, and that occult knowledge must be openly proclaimed amongst men as Spiritual Science. He set conditions to this "open" teaching. The seer should reveal nothing until by long and repeated meditation he had completely absorbed its significance, and then, only if he could express it in thought-forms intelligible to his hearers.

In doing this Steiner broke no vow of secrecy, for his spiritual knowledge had come by self-initiation on the basis of his own natural clairvoyance. There were some who criticised his decision, and the problems involved in the dissemination of his lectures illustrate the dangers that he faced. We cannot, however, be too grateful that he took the initial risk, and that he and his followers took a further risk in allowing the publication of his lectures. For in them is given that vast application of the principles of Spiritual Science in almost every sphere of human interest and activity, which offers a field of endless exploration and discovery to all students.

It only requires, however, a little reflection to see how easily mistakes or conflicting statements of detail may arise in the lectures. There is first of all the variability in the quality of the stenographer or of his or her understanding of the subject of the lecture; then there is the element of error in the reduction of the shorthand to German without any revision by the lecturer, and, again, in its translation into English. The student, therefore, should begin his study with the books carefully edited by Steiner for publication, until he has mastered the principles of Anthroposophy. Moreover, when he passes on to the lectures, he should regard them as fields of application or of deeper revelation, and should not treat them as being literally exact in all their detail. Steiner himself wrote: "It will be necessary to remember that there are errors in the lectures which I did not revise."[1] He mentions the hostile criticism that was sometimes levelled against him by those outside Anthroposophy, on the ground of some quotation from one of his lectures.

From another point of view there is a great advantage in the impossibility of relying on the *ipsissima verba* of the lectures, for it relieves Steiner's teaching from that "binding authority", which would have cramped the freedom and independence of research and discovery to which he called his fellow-men. One of the criticisms that is levelled against Anthroposophy, even in responsible quarters, is that Rudolf Steiner is accorded unqualified adulation by his followers. "With many of them the words 'The Doctor said it', are regarded as sufficient to close any dispute," one critic writes.

[1] *Story of My Life*, p. 322.

Now adulation is not confined to Steiner and his followers. It is found in all sorts of human associations, from politics to psychology.

Nor is it unnatural that ordinary people, who have learned through Steiner the profound truths of Man and the Universe, should have a sense of reverent acceptance in regard to his utterances, when so distinguished a seer and thinker as Edouard Schuré confessed to the overwhelming sense of spiritual authority conveyed by his speaking.[1]

But, repellent as adulation is to the critical outsider, it was no less distasteful to Steiner himself. The following passage is taken from one of his lecture-cycles.

> I beg of you to accept nothing I have ever said or ever shall say, on or in blind faith. It is possible, even before a man has reached the stage of clairvoyance, to test what is obtained through clairvoyant observation. I beseech you to disaccustom yourselves from the principle of authority, for that principle would be an evil one for us. . . . I count upon the communications made from Spiritual Science not being believed, but *proved*, not superficially only, but ever more and more conscientiously. Take all that the most modern science with the newest methods can offer you, take everything which historical or religious investigations have yielded; the more you test Spiritual Science, the more your testing will confirm it. You must take nothing on authority.[2]

Another objection that is sometimes made to the serious consideration of Steiner's teaching is the fact that, although his writings date from the early eighties, and although his output in writings and lectures was phenomenal right up to his death in 1925, yet he has made little impact on the general scientific world of our day, and in our own country his teaching is not seriously considered by the majority of the leaders of thought: indeed, in some quarters, it is hardly known.

[1] See p. 66.

[2] *The Mission of Folk-Souls* (Steiner), pp. 143, 144.

The reason for this is not hard to find. It is due to the special nature of Steiner's teaching and to the social and political conditions of the last fifty years. The years from 1880 to the outbreak of the first world war in 1914 were the hey-day of complacent scientific materialism. In Germany this attitude was pursued with a conviction that would not give consideration to any world-concept that was based on the objective reality of the supersensible. It would have been inconceivable in those days that any reputable scientist should call upon his fellow-scientists to give serious consideration to the phenomena of telepathy and faith-healing, as Dr. Carrel did in the thirties, or postulate the development of new senses of perception, as Sir James Jeans did in the forties. The only sympathetic audience that Steiner could find, as we have seen, was, at first the Theosophists, and then a slowly-growing group of people who felt the spiritual truth and urgency of his message. But by 1914 he had a wide following in Europe and was beginning to be known in Great Britain, though very few of his works had at that time been translated into English. All this was brought to a standstill by the first world war.

After the war he began to be much more widely known and appreciated in Germany, and he gave several courses of lectures, by interpretation, in England. Anthroposophy was, however, very much centred in Dornach, and was quite unknown to the English public.

The years after Steiner's death were difficult years for the Anthroposophical Movement, for the Nazi Party very much suppressed its activities in Germany, and, in Dornach, an unhappy division which arose amongst Steiner's followers weakened its outward development. Meanwhile the Anthroposophical Society in Great Britain had been founded in 1923, and in the following years two schools were opened and a curative and agricultural centre established. In the thirties the work was stimulated by the arrival in this country of a number of distinguished continental Anthroposophists, refugees from Nazi tyranny. The translations into English, however, were held up by lack of resources and then by the six years of the second world war. Since the end of the war the work of translation and publication has gone forward and the activities of the Anthroposophical Societies in Great Britain and in other English-speaking countries have developed in lectures and conferences, while the number of schools and curative institutions and other centres of Anthroposophical activity have multiplied. At the same time it is true that, for most British people, Anthroposophy is still regarded as a foreign movement of which they have no knowledge. It is in an attempt to meet this need, that this book has been written.

On the Continent more public interest is awakening, probably because men and women there are more urgently confronted with the bewildering problems of the present time. A few weeks ago a German lecturer at one of our universities, who is not an Anthroposophist, said to me: "No one can understand the situation in Germany today without a knowledge of Anthroposophy. It is becoming one of the leading movements of thought there."

No one with any seriousness of mind can escape the feeling of momentous crisis at this moment in the affairs of mankind. Besides the tense political and sociological oppositions of which we have spoken, and the rapidly changing spiritual relationships between East and West, there is the growing colour problem and the rising nationalism manifest in Africa and Asia. Transcending all sectional interests, there is the universal problem of man's relation to Nature, with the looming uncertainty of the adequacy of food-resources. Above all, there is the threat of the enormously destructive power of modern scientific knowledge, a sword of Damocles suspended over a frightened humanity. Thirty years ago Steiner spoke again and again of the critical years for mankind at the beginning of the second half of the century, and of the tremendous issues for good and evil that were dependent upon man waking to the knowledge of the reality of spirit. It is remarkable how, in the last few years, similar utterances have been made by leading thinkers, all of whom feel that mankind has reached a stage when there must be a new beginning, an upsurgence of new powers and of a new level of understanding. We have already spoken of Sir James Jeans' indication of the need for higher senses and of Maurice Nicoll's defence of the search for higher states of consciousness. So too J. G. Bennett, in his book, *The Crisis in Human Affairs*, writes of:

> the general feeling of expectancy which we can trace in books written about scientific knowledge at the present time. It is constantly suggested that some new way of thinking is about to emerge. . . . The first condition that must be fulfilled (before a new epoch can begin) is that knowledge and guidance should come to us from a higher level. . . . We must place the hope of the world in a fresh Revelation of the Divine Purpose to Mankind and prepare ourselves to be ready to receive it.[1]

In the last of his Gifford Lectures, recently delivered at Edinburgh, Professor A. J. Toynbee (as reported in *The Times*) declared that for the last two or three centuries we have been probing the mystery of the universe from the mathematico-physical standpoint which was adopted by our Western fore-fathers, when, at the end of the seventeenth century, they deliberately abandoned a theological standpoint, because it had led their predecessors into controversy, strife and blood-shed. Today, he said, the time has come for us, in our turn, to abandon the exclusively mathematico-physical standpoint, that has armed mankind with deadly weapons, but has not redeemed it from original sin. We need to make a new start, by returning to the spiritual outlook that was abandoned in the seventeenth century, without repeating its fault by throwing away the technological and scientific achievements of the last two and a half centuries.

Steiner goes even further than this in his continual declaration that the rediscovery of the spirit must not be a return to the past, but must arise out of a development of true scientific thinking.

But the most striking appraisement of the situation is that given by Nicolas Berdyaev in his posthumous book, *The Realm of the Spirit and the Realm of Cæsar*. It is remarkable how

[1] *The Crisis in Human Affairs*, by J. G. Bennett, pp. 147.

analogous to Steiner's is his diagnosis of the present situation. He divides human history into four periods, from the point of view of man's relation to the Cosmos. The first is the age of magic and myth; in the second, man begins to be free of cosmic powers, and civilisations arise. The third is the age of the scientific and mechanical control of Nature; while the fourth (the present age) is that of the disruption of the Cosmic Order, the terrified and terrifying power of man over Nature. It is the Age of Technics, "a world made by man, not existing in Nature." This is the exact description of the Ahrimanic world, of which Steiner so often speaks as threatening the spiritual destiny of Man and the Earth. It needs, to meet it, Berdyaev declares, "a spiritual movement, the work of freedom".

The similarity of diagnosis and remedy to that of Steiner is still more apparent in the final page of the book.

> The world is moving through darkness towards a new spirituality and a new mysticism. The new mysticism will not consider this objectivised world as final reality. . . . In it will be revealed a true gnosis . . . and all the tormenting contradictions and divisions will be resolved in the new mysticism, which will be deeper than religions and ought to unite them. It will be the victory over false forms of social mysticism, the victory of the realm of the Spirit over the realm of Cæsar. . . . The final triumph of the realm of Spirit presupposes a change in the structure of human consciousness. This can be envisaged only eschatologically.

It is a statement of sober fact to say that Rudolf Steiner had arrived at this diagnosis fifty years and more ago. It was in 1886, in his early twenties, that he had come to the decision, posited by Maurice Nicoll, that the way past the apparent limitation of human knowledge was to be found in the evolution of a higher level of consciousness. As we have seen, he spent his whole life expounding the possibility of this, and outlining the spiritual remedies that will meet the situation. In doing this he cannot be charged—as he sometimes has been charged—with an arrogant assumption that man has his destiny entirely in his own hands, and is independent of divine help, such as J. G. Bennett speaks of, or as is implicit in Berdyaev's words that the new age "can be envisaged only eschatologically". No one has spoken more explicitly than Steiner of the constant work of the whole spirit-world in forwarding the eternal destiny of humanity; no one has more strongly asserted the complete dependence of man upon the unique work of Christ. But what others look for in an eschatological hope of which they have no immediate certainty, Steiner saw as a day that was already dawning, the redemption of human thinking that was the culmination of the redemptive work of Christ, and which He is at this moment offering to mankind.

The secret of the future lies in the transformation of man, by his rediscovery of himself. This is expressed in a dramatic and arresting way by Charles Morgan in his play *The River-Line.* One of the characters is describing the discussion of a little group of fighting men in their secret hide-out in France, under the guidance of that remarkable soldier-philosopher, Heron:

> The world, we said, was in desperate need of a period of creative pause. We debated the meaning and the possibility of that, ranging up and down history for parallel instances. Never until now, Heron argued, had there been the same necessity, because never before had man's knowledge so outrun his wisdom—his capacity to relate one knowledge to another knowledge, his capacity to synthesize. And never before had the whole world been maddened as it was now by a sense of frustration, of being separated from Nature and from the very sources of self-renewal. The danger was much greater than what was ordinarily called a breakdown of civilisation; civilisations had vanished before. The danger was of the disintegration of the human personality, the going-mad and the withering of man, because he was distracted and cut off from his roots. "I mean by a creative pause," Heron said, "a period in which man

regains his lost sense of origin, of rhythm and continuity, and in which he begins again to feel the sap rise. The idea of sap and the idea of fruit are not separable without madness, as spirit and nature are not, and the world in which we now live is obsessed by the idea of fruit—and not even by the idea of bearing it, but by the idea of consuming it. That is the insanity into which the economic interpretation of history has led us. Existence is economic, but life is not; that radical and vital contact has to be renewed."

In no words could the situation have been better expressed, for they arise out of the soul and mind of the ordinary man. The great need of the world, to which Steiner points the way, is man's rediscovery of himself, in discovering the reality of spirit within him that links him to the world about him and to the Divine above him.

The words of ancient Mystery-wisdom ring out again, as a challenge to the blatant materialism, the complacent agnosticism, and the bewildered uncertainty of our day: "MAN, KNOW THYSELF!"

INDEX